W9-DFI-693

AEROSPACE
S C I E N C E
The Exploration of Space
STUDENT WORKBOOK
Second Edition

Doug Kirkpatrick

Carol Larson

Doug Miller

This textbook has been published for the

UNITED STATES AIR FORCE

JUNIOR RESERVE OFFICER TRAINING CORPS

The McGraw-Hill Companies, Inc.
Boston   Burr Ridge, IL   Dubuque, IA   Madison, WI   New York
San Francisco   St. Louis   Bangkok   Bogotá   Caracas   Kuala Lumpur
Lisbon   London   Madrid   Mexico City   Milan   Montreal   New Delhi
Santiago   Seoul   Singapore   Sydney   Taipei   Toronto

V-6325W

AEROSPACE SCIENCE
The Exploration of Space, STUDENT WORKBOOK
V-6325W

Materials were created by Coyote Enterprises, Inc., 14 Thayer Road, Colorado Springs, Colorado 80906. Edited by ToucanEd Inc.,1280 17th Ave., Suite 102, Santa Cruz, California 95062.

   4 5 6 7 8 9 0   QPD QPD 0 9 8 7

ISBN 0-07-312466-4

Project Manager: Paula Kefover
Air Force JROTC Project Manager and Editor: Naomi Mitchell
McGraw-Hill Editor: Judith Wetherington
Editors: Doug Kirkpatrick, Carol Larson, and Joel Miller
Production Editor: Carrie Braun
Cover Design: Maggie Lytle
Printer/Binder: Quebecor World

TABLE OF CONTENTS

Preface

Introduction

Aerospace Science: The Exploration of Space is an exciting new textbook about space. Together with the text, the student workbook will guide you through an all new world of satellites, orbits, space environments and travel to other planets. By applying yourself using these learning aids, you can find great insights into how and why we go to so much trouble to put complicated satellites into orbit. The Exploration of Space text and workbook will prepare you for advanced courses in aerospace engineering and science.

Student Strategy

The text covers a lot of material and you can use this student workbook to minimize your efforts focusing your attention on key information in the chapters. Yes, if you use this student workbook wisely, you can save yourself lots of time and get better grades!

We recommend you read a section from the text, review the Vocabulary words at the beginning of each section and the Key Concepts at the end of each section, and complete the associated section in the student workbook. By actually seeing the material three times your learning will improve! The "Things to Think About" at the end of each section are repeated in Section F of this student workbook because they ask about important principles that will improve your learning.

Workbook Layout

Each section in the text has a corresponding section in this student workbook and you can easily find the proper section in the student workbook by referring to the Table of Contents.

PART A of this student workbook section has the Vocabulary words (Define, Describe, or Identify) from the text with space for your written definition. You may search for the definition in the text in the section itself or refer to the Glossary at the end of the text. Either way you should be able to easily find the appropriate definitions in a short period of time.

PART B of this student workbook asks you to Fill in the Blanks with one word in each blank. You can check the text for the exact words to use in the blanks, if necessary. Occasionally, you'll find that more than one word fits in the blank. Usually, one word is a little better than the other and the text has the exact word to use.

PART C of this student workbook is Multiple Choice, so circle the answer that most correctly answers the question. Only one answer is correct for each question. All of the questions come from the sections in the text.

PART D of this student workbook is Matching. As the heading states, match the item in colun A with its description in column B. You may use each letter only once but you typically won'1 use all of the letters.

PART E of this student workbook is True or False. Place a T or F in the blank based on wheth the statement is true or false. Referring to the text will help you decide.

PART F of this student workbook has the Short Answers (Things to Think About) questions. of the "Things to Think About" questions that are included at the end of each section of the tex are included here for your use. There's a small amount of space under each question for your answer.

PART G of this student workbook is a special List or Describe section. These questions are meant to make you think and apply the text material. The answers aren't always in the text. Ir some instances, we ask for your opinion, so you can discuss your ideas with your classmates ai instructor. Not all chapters have Part G.

You can learn a lot by using the student workbook along with your text, so we hope you truly enjoy learning about space exploration!

We welcome your comments or suggestions concerning this student workbook. Please forwar them to HQ AFOATS/CRJD, 551 East Maxwell Blvd., Maxwell AFB, AL 36112-6106.

UNIT 1: Introduction to Space Exploration

Chapter 1 Space in Our Lives

Section 1.1. Why Space?

(Homework Problems: A1; C1-C4)

A. Define, Describe, or Identify (Vocabulary):

1. Free fall

2. Gravity

3. Ozone concentration layer

4. Remote-sensing

5. Scintillation

6. Ultraviolet radiation

B. Fill in the Blanks:

Fill in the blank with the word or words necessary to complete the statement.

1. Space is the ultimate _____ _____ that offers a global perspective for many useful purposes.

2. The bounty of the Solar System offers an untapped reserve of _____ and _____ to sustain people beyond the cradle of Earth.

3. In modern times, a collection of communication satellites in _____-_____ _____ forms a global cellular telephone network.

4. Urban planners use images from spacecraft such as _____ and _____ for planning land development.

C. Multiple Choice:

Circle the letter that correctly answers the question or completes the statement.

1. Which of the following best describes the experience some (in error) call "zero gravity?"

    a. Weightlessness

    b. Free fall

    c. No contact forces

    d. All of the above

2. We could take _____ and _____ from the Moon's surface, as resources for a colony of explorers.

    a. hydrogen, coal

    b. iron, uranium

    c. oxygen, aluminum

    d. nitrogen, chlorine

3. Why do people want to explore space as the final frontier?

    a. Economic expansion

    b. Limitless challenge

    c. Increases in technology

    d. All of the above

4. _____ satellites help us talk to each other anywhere on the planet.

    a. Communication

    b. Remote sensing

    c. Navigation

    d. Exploration

D. Matching:

Match the item in Column A with the description in Column B. You may use each item from Column B only once, but you won't use all of them.

Column A	*Column B*
1. Scintillation _____	a. Mixing metal alloys in free fall
2. Hubble Space Telescope, Gamma Ray Observatory, Chandra X-ray Observatory _____	b. Pinpoints position for ships, planes, cars, trucks, and hikers
3. Echo I, Palapa A, Milstar _____	c. Apollo moon landings
4. Remote-sensing satellites _____	d. Atmospheric blurring of starlight
5. Global Positioning System _____	e. Helps map makers, city planners, and weather forecasters
6. Voyager, Magellan, and Mars Pathfinder _____	f. Bringing new views and understanding of deep space
	g. Spacecraft that have explored the solar system
	h. Communications satellites based in space

E. True/False:

Place a **T** in the blank if the statement is true, and an **F** in the blank if it is false.

_____ 1. Space can be many things to many people, which draws us to it as the final frontier.

_____ 2. In 1945, Arthur C. Clarke proposed sending navigation satellites into orbit to support the military.

_____ 3. From space, spacecraft can detect an object's temperature and composition (type of material).

_____ 4. Humans can't tolerate long-term space travel, so astronauts must return to Earth every few days.

F. Short Answers (Things to Think About):

Write a short answer to each question.

1. What five unique advantages of space make its exploration very important for modern society?

2. What are the four primary space missions in use today? Give an example of how each has affected, or could affect, your life.

G. List or Describe:

1. What kinds of data do sensors collect in space to watch the world's environment?

2. Discuss future missions that could exploit the free-fall environment of space.

3. Discuss future space missions that could exploit resources on the Moon.

4. What benefits can we expect from using the International Space Station for ten years?

Chapter 1 Space in Our Lives

Section 1.2. Elements of a Space Mission

(Homework Problems A4-A6; A18-A26; E1-E4)

A. Define, Describe, or Identify (Vocabulary):

1. Astronautics

2. Constellation

3. Field-of-view (FOV)

4. Flight-control team

5. Flight director

6. Launch vehicle

7. Mission

8. Mission director

9. Mission management and operations

10. Mission objective

11. Mission operations concept

12. Mission operations system

13. Mission operations team

14. Mission statement

15. Mission users

16. Operations director

17. Orbit

18. Parking orbit

19. Payload

20. Space mission architecture

21. Spacecraft bus

22. Stages

23. Subject

24. Swath width

25. Thrusters

26. Trajectory

27. Transfer orbit

28. Upper stage

B. Fill in the Blanks:

Fill in the blank with the word or words necessary to complete the statement.

1. At the heart of the space mission architecture is the _____.

2. We design payloads to work with a mission's main focus, called the _____.

3. The _____ _____ has an important role in linking all elements of a space mission.

4. Mission _____ lead space missions from the beginning.

C. Multiple Choice:

Circle the letter that correctly answers the question or completes the statement.

1. The mission operations system includes the ground- and space-based _____ needed to coordinate all other elements of the space mission architecture.

    a. people and procedures
    b. payloads
    c. framework
    d. machinery

2. Mission management and operations for a space mission include _____.

    a. the hardware and software at the operations center

    b. the remote data relay station

    c. the launch vehicle on the launch pad with the spacecraft attached

    d. a huge group of people doing their space-related jobs well

3. A launch vehicle follows a precise _____ to efficiently lift a spacecraft off Earth and through the atmosphere.

    a. trajectory

    b. orbit

    c. mission operations system

    d. profile

D. Matching:

Match the item in Column A with the description in Column B. You may use each item from Column B only once, but you won't use all of them.

Column A	*Column B*
1. Space mission architecture _____	a. Coordinates a spacecraft's activities in orbit
2. Satellite constellation _____	b. Space Shuttle and Ariane V
3. Launch vehicles _____	c. Rocket engine thrusters
4. Flight-control team _____	d. Global Positioning System
	e. Collection of spacecraft, orbits, launch vehicles, operations networks, etc.

E. True/False:

Place a **T** in the blank if the statement is true, and an **F** in the blank if it is false.

_____ 1. When we see a weather map on the nightly news, we should remember the complex network supporting the weather satellites that make the images.

_____ 2. A spacecraft's payload is the part that performs the mission.

_____ 3. A launch vehicle usually goes straight up during launch to gain altitude and get through the atmosphere that slows it down.

_____ 4. A parking orbit usually is filled with satellites waiting to move to their mission orbits.

_____ 5. A spacecraft's thruster helps keep it in orbit and maintain its orientation.

F. Short Answers (Things to Think About):

Write a short answer to each question.

1. What three things does the mission statement tell us?

2. What are the elements of a space mission?

3. List the two basic parts of a spacecraft and discuss what they do for the mission.

4. What is an orbit? How does changing the size of an orbit affect the energy required to get into it and the swath width available to any payload in this orbit?

5. What is a parking orbit? A transfer orbit?

6. Describe what an upper stage does.

7. Why do we say that the operations network is the "glue" that holds the other elements together?

8. What is the mission management and operations element?

G. List or Describe:

1. You hear a television commentator say the Space Shuttle's missions are a waste of money. How would you respond to this charge?

Chapter 2 Exploring Space

Section 2.1. Entering Space

(Homework Problems: B2, C1-C5)

A. Define, Describe, or Identify (Vocabulary):

1. Ballistic missile

2. Communication satellite

3. Cosmic rays

4. Cosmonaut

5. Electromagnetic spectrum

6. Interplanetary probes

7. Magnetic field

8. Suborbital

B. Fill in the Blanks:

Fill in the blank with the word or words necessary to complete the statement.

1. American scientist _____ _____ worked on liquid rocket engines and launched the first liquid-fuel rocket in 1926.

2. The _____ rocket was the world's first ballistic missile.

3. The former Soviet Union launched the first artificial satellite, named _____, in 1957.

4. The first American to orbit in space was _____ _____, who completed only three orbits because of a problem with his capsule's heat shield.

5. _____ _____ and _____ _____ were the first two men to set foot on the Moon on July 20, 1969.

6. _____ 1 and 2 took better photos of Jupiter, Saturn, Uranus and their moons than Viking 1 and 2.

C. Multiple Choice:

Circle the letter that correctly answers the question or completes the statement.

1. In the early 19th Century, rockets were instruments of _____, used in the Napoleonic Wars and the War of 1812.

    a. science

    b. war

    c. exploration

    d. observation

2. The deaf Russian schoolteacher, _____ _____, studied Newton's Laws and proposed using liquid rockets to get into space, long before rockets were big enough to do so.

    a. Yuri Gagarin

    b. Jules Verne

    c. Hermann Oberth

    d. Konstantin Tsiolkovsky

3. Wernher von Braun was the main designer for the _____ and _____ rockets, one built for war and one to launch Apollo missions to the Moon.

    a. V-2, Saturn V

    b. Saturn V, Space Shuttle

    c. X-15, Saturn V

    d. Saturn V, Ariane V

4. Echo I was America's first _____ satellite that reflected voice and picture signals.

    a. navigation

    b. communication

    c. manned

    d. remote sensing

5. President John F. Kennedy committed the U.S. to land a man on the _____ and return him safely to _____.

    a. Mars, Earth

    b. Space station, Earth

    c. Moon, Earth

    d. Venus, Mars

D. Matching:

Match the person or space system in Column A with the description in Column B. You may use an item from Column B only once, but you won't use all of them.

Column A	*Column B*
1. Jules Verne ___	a. Tracks Earth resources from space
2. Ballistic missile ___	b. First U.S. space station
3. Redstone rocket ___	c. Wrote *From the Earth to the Moon*
4. Explorer I ___	d. First American to orbit Earth
5. John Glenn ___	e. V-2 was the world's first
6. Valentina Tereshkova ___	f. Carried first U.S. satellite into space
7. Landsat ___	g. First woman in space
	h. Spent more than a year in space
	i. First U.S. satellite

E. True/False:

Place a **T** in the blank if the statement is true, and an **F** in the blank if it is false.

_____ 1. Rockets date back to 1232 A.D, when Chinese warriors defended their homeland.

_____ 2. British Colonel William Congreve first used crude rockets in World War I.

_____ 3. U.S. soldiers captured V-2 rockets and German rocket scientists after World War II and brought them to the U.S.

_____ 4. NASA was formed in 1958, partly to increase the U.S. emphasis on science education in schools.

_____ 5. Millions of people from all over the world watched when Neil Armstrong stepped onto the Moon in July 1969.

_____ 6. The U.S. space station, Skylab, came from a converted Russian Soyuz rocket.

F. Short Answers (Things to Think About):

Write a short answer to each question.

1. What are the different ways people can explore space?

2. Why might we call 1957-1965 the years of Russian dominance in space?

3. What was the main legacy of the Apollo missions to the Moon?

G. List or Describe:

1. Do we need to launch men and women into space or should we rely exclusively on probes and Earth-based instruments to explore space?

2. By exploring space, can we learn anything that can help us solve problems on Earth?

Chapter 2 Exploring Space

Section 2.2. Space Comes of Age

(Homework Problems: A5, C1-C6)

A. Define, Describe, or Identify (Vocabulary):

1. Force Projection

2. Interstellar

3. Interstellar dust

4. Microsatellites

5. Reusable vehicles

6. Solar corona

7. Solar wind

8. Space Control

9. Synthetic-aperture radar

B. Fill in the Blanks:

Fill in the blank with the word or words necessary to complete the statement.

1. During the 1990s, _____'s synthetic-aperture radar mapped more than 98% of Venus's surface.

2. The Lunar Prospector orbited the Moon and discovered vast amounts of

   _____ _____.

3. The _____ spacecraft took pictures of a comet that broke into pieces and smashed into Jupiter.

4. The _____ _____ _____ is a cooperative space venture with 16 nations contributing to its long-term success with astronauts, modules, and experiments.

5. Early warning, communications, and intelligence gathering are all _____ uses of space.

C. Multiple Choice:

Circle the letter that correctly answers the question or completes the statement.

1. Which of the following is <u>not</u> one of the four major trends in space from the 1990s?
   a. Space International
   b. Space Science, Big and Small
   c. Space Incorporated
   d. Space Inexpensive

2. The _____ _____ landed on Mars and explored its surface for several weeks.
   a. Global Surveyor
   b. Mars Pathfinder
   c. Magellan spacecraft
   d. Space Shuttle

3. Launched in 1990, the _____ _____ _____
   photographed new and wondrous galactic events such as star births and deaths,
   colliding galaxies, and enormous black holes.

   a. International Space Station

   b. Global Positioning System

   c. Hubble Space Telescope

   d. Mir Space Station

4. The interplanetary spacecraft, _____, orbited Saturn and positioned
   a probe to land on Titan—Saturn's Earth-sized moon—to search for life.

   a. Ulysses

   b. Galileo

   c. Magellan

   d. Cassini

5. Identify three countries that joined the "space club" by starting national space
   programs in the 1990s.

   a. Israel, Brazil, and India

   b. Indonesia, Costa Rica, Canada

   c. Spain, France, and Morocco

   d. Russia, United States, and Japan

6. Pegasus is a _____ launch vehicle that launches from
   _____.

   a. large, Kodiak Island, Alaska

   b. small, Cape Kennedy

   c. large, Cape Kennedy

   d. small, a mother plane

D. Matching:

Match the item in Column A with the description in Column B. You may use an item from Column B only once, but you won't use all of them.

Column A	*Column B*
1. New high ground ____	a. Reliable Russian launch vehicles
2. Zarya Control Module ____	b. Located polar ice on the Moon
3. Ulysses ____	c. One of four major trends in space in the 1990s
4. Global Positioning System ____	d. Located a huge black hole in the galaxy Centaurus A
5. Proton, Zenit, and Tsyklon ____	e. Latest system of military communication satellites
6. Global Reach ____	f. In a solar-polar orbit measuring the corona and solar winds
7. Milstar ____	g. First element of the International Space Station
	h. Helps weapons hit their targets
	i. Uses space communication satellites to help deploy troops and weapons worldwide

E. True/False:

Place a **T** in the blank if the statement is true, and an **F** in the blank if it is false.

_____ 1. NASA uses the Space Shuttle to repair orbiting satellites, launch interplanetary spacecraft, and haul modules and material to the International Space Station.

_____ 2. As the 1990s began, the U.S. focused on many small space projects, but no big projects.

_____ 3. The U.S. space program did <u>not</u> interact with the Russian space program after the fall of the Soviet Union.

_____ 4. Scientists may find life in the solar system: microorganisms in the oceans on Europa—one of Jupiter's moons.

_____ 5. The European Space Agency and NASA worked together on the Solar and Heliospheric Observatory that studies the Sun's internal structure, its outer atmosphere, and the solar wind.

_____ 6. Comet dust, collected by the Stardust satellite, showed conclusively that comets and our Moon contain the same elements.

F. Short Answers (Things to Think About):

Write a short answer to each question.

1. What are some of the key discoveries made during the 1990s with the Hubble Space Telescope?

2. Why should we build an International Space Station? What are its benefits and drawbacks?

3. How might we reduce costs of a mission carrying a crew to Mars?

4. If humans venture to Mars, which planet should we visit next?

5. Why are commercial companies becoming interested in space?

6. What missions do militaries hope to accomplish in space?

7. Should weapons be deployed in space?

8. Besides Earth, where are we most likely to find life in our solar system?

G. List or Describe:

1. Has the search for extraterrestrial beings been important to the development of astronomy? Should we continue searching for other life forms and inhabited planets?

Chapter 2 Exploring Space

Section 2.3. Organizing the Air Force for Space Operations

(Homework Problems: A1, A5, A12, D1-D6)

A. Define, Describe, or Identify (Vocabulary):

1. Aerospace

2. Air Force's mission

3. Air Force Space Command (AFSPC)

4. Baker Nunn cameras

5. Ballistic Missile Early Warning System

6. Consolidated Space Operations Center (CSOC)

7. Defense Meteorological Satellite Program

8. Defense Support Program

9. Gaither Commission

10. Milstar

11. Minitrack

12. Moonwatch

13. North American Air Defense Command (NORAD)

14. Optical tracking network

15. Persian Gulf War

16. Phased-array radar

17. Satellite telemetry

18. Sputnik

19. Strategic Air Command (SAC)

20. Tactical Air Command (TAC)

21. Vanguard

B. Fill in the Blanks:

Fill in the blank with the word or words necessary to complete the statement.

1. In 1946, a RAND Corporation report suggested launching satellites into orbit to complete _____ studies, _____, and _____ Earth.

2. In a race with the former Soviet Union, the U.S. developed its first two intercontinental ballistic missiles, the _____ and _____.

3. In the U.S., the launch delay for the _____ rocket in 1957, and the Soviets' launch of Sputnik, made Americans worry about a growing _____ _____ between us.

4. While several U.S. military and civilian groups were trying to launch our first satellite, the North American Air Defense Command (NORAD) began operations to defend the airspace over the _____ and _____.

5. Air Force General _____ _____ _____ used proposals and high-level meetings in the late 1970s and early 1980s to push his idea for a new command: the _____ _____.

6. During the mid-80s to early 90s, space missions, such as _____, _____ _____, and _____ _____, were combined in one command.

7. In 1995-1996, Air Force personnel in _____ _____ _____ deployed with U.S. war fighters in Bosnia to coordinate effective use of military space systems.

C. Multiple Choice:

Circle the letter that correctly answers the question or completes the statement.

1. Which of the following was an early rocket program in the U.S. following World War II?

    a. V-2

    b. Orbiter

    c. Vanguard

    d. All of the above

2. Early satellite-tracking efforts relied on _____ _____ cameras and amateur _____ to see orbiting satellites.

    a. handheld photographic, radars

    b. Baker-Nunn, astronomers

    c. handheld video, observers

    d. hometown observers, trackers

3. In 1959, the U.S. Air Force coined the word _____ to describe its mission that included space.

    a. defense

    b. warfighter

    c. aerospace

    d. satellite

4. Which of the following was a location for one of the three U.S.-built ballistic-missile-tracking radars that also tracked satellites in the early 1960s?

    a. Fylingsdale Moor, England

    b. Hansom AFB, Massachusetts

    c. Vandenberg AFB, California

    d. Patrick AFB, Florida

5. In the mid-1960s, new radar technology in the U.S. produced the first _____-_____ radar at Eglin AFB, Florida.

    a. long-range

    b. high-frequency

    c. Baker-Nunn

    d. phased-array

6. The _____ antiballistic-missile site in North Dakota closed in 1976 because Congress objected to its questionable effectiveness.

    a. Minot

    b. PARCS

    c. Safeguard

    d. Cheyenne

7. Which of the following was not a military space mission controlled from the Consolidated Space Operations Center at Falcon AFB, CO, after it opened in 1985?

    a. Global Positioning System

    b. Defense Meteorological Satellite Program

    c. Milstar communications satellites

    d. Landsat

8. In the first space war, military satellites directly supported U.S. combatants with which of the following space systems?

    a. Global Positioning System

    b. Defense Meteorological Satellite System

    c. Early-warning satellites

    d. All of the above

D. Matching:

Match the item in Column A with the description in Column B. You may use an item from Column B only once, but you won't use all of them.

Column A	*Column B*
1. V-2 ____	a. Alerted by early warning satellites
2. 474L System Program Office ____	b. Activation of Space Command
3. Eglin AFB, FL, radar ____	c. Accurate weapons targeting
4. Global Positioning System ____	d. Developed early-warning radars
5. Patriot missiles ____	e. First operational SLBM tracker
6. September 1, 1982 ____	f. German design, tested for spaceflight
	g. Launched first satellite

E. True/False:

Place a **T** in the blank if the statement is true, and an **F** in the blank if it is false.

_____ 1. Seven months after the first big launch failure at Cape Canaveral, the U.S. government created the National Aeronautics and Space Administration.

_____ 2. In 1959, the Chief of Naval Operations suggested that the U.S. military form a unified space command.

_____ 3. In the 1980s, four phased-array radars watched the U.S. eastern, western, and southern coastlines for enemy surface ships carrying missiles.

_____ 4. The Air Force Chief of Staff changed the AF mission to include air and space in 1992.

F. Short Answers (Things to Think About):

Write a short answer to each question.

1. What group of scientists shaped the design of the earliest rockets in the United States after World War II?

2. What events in the former Soviet Union caused U.S. officials to distrust them and push the military to develop intercontinental ballistic missiles?

3. What did the Gaither Commission find to be the state of U.S. national defense? What did the Government do about it?

4. Why do you think the Sputnik launch caught the United States and the rest of the world by surprise?

5. In the 1960s, what were the two main parts of national defense that directly related to space?

6. What military thinking came together in 1982 that led to Space Command?

7. What space missions did the new Space Command combine under its control during its first 20 years of its existence?

8. Air Force Space Command has the job of preparing for space warfare. Is there a logical reason for military warfighters to live in and defend our nation from space?

Chapter 3 The Space Environment

Section 3.1. Cosmic Perspective

(Homework Problems: A1, B1, B3, E1-E4)

A. Define, Describe, or Identify (Vocabulary):

1. Charged particles

2. Cosmic year

3. Electromagnetic (EM) radiation

4. Galactic center

5. Light year

6. Nuclear fusion

7. Plasma

8. Solar flare

9. Solar particle events

10. Wavelength

B. Fill in the Blanks:

Fill in the blank with the word or words necessary to complete the statement.

1. Jet aircraft can fly us high into the atmosphere, but we need a _____ to get into space.

2. At the current burn rate, our Sun has enough hydrogen to last about _____ _____ years.

3. Light and all electromagnetic radiation travel at the speed of light, _____ kilometers per second.

4. Within our Sun's fiery core (1 million degrees Celsius) swirls a hot soup of electrons and protons, known as a _____.

5. Besides the nine planets, we are aware of dozens of _____ and thousands of _____ existing in our solar system.

6. The closest galaxy to our Milky Way Galaxy is _____, which is two million light years away.

C. Multiple Choice:

Circle the letter that correctly answers the question or completes the statement.

1. Spacecraft in low-Earth orbit run into _____ molecules that slow them down and shorten their orbital lifetimes.

    a. carbon

    b. air

    c. uranium

    d. water

2. Space Shuttle orbits are just barely above the _____.

    a. airliner routes

    b. Moon

    c. atmosphere

    d. clouds

3. For each second the Sun burns, it could supply all the energy needs of the U.S. for
    _____ years.

    a. 10
    b. 2500
    c. 253 thousand
    d. 624 million

4. The colors of the rainbow (visible light) are just a small part of the
    _____ _____.

    a. electromagnetic spectrum
    b. sunlight's wavelengths
    c. Sun's emissions
    d. all of the above

5. Which of the following is <u>not</u> one of the mighty gas-giant planets?

    a. Mercury
    b. Saturn
    c. Jupiter
    d. Uranus

6. Astronomers think our solar system is about _____ years old.

    a. 2.2 million
    b. 1.2 billion
    c. 4.8 billion
    d. 140 billion

D. Matching:

Match the item in Column A with the description in Column B. You may use an item from Column B only once, but you won't use all of them.

Column A

1. Our Sun _____
2. Colors of the rainbow _____
3. Milky Way Galaxy _____
4. Venus _____
5. Proxima Centauri _____
6. Jupiter _____

Column B

a. Earth-like planet
b. Spiral shaped
c. Gas giant planet
d. Small part of the range of electromagnetic waves
e. 150 million kilometers
f. Fueled by nuclear fusion
g. 4.22 light years away

E. True/False:

Place a **T** in the blank if the statement is true, and an **F** in the blank if it is false.

_____ 1. Our Sun's fusion process produces electromagnetic radiation and charged particles.

_____ 2. More than 300 billion stars are in our close neighborhood, the Milky Way Galaxy.

_____ 3. A solar flare gives off about as much energy as a nuclear weapon.

_____ 4. Our Sun and solar system revolve around the center of the Andromeda Galaxy.

F. Short Answers (Things to Think About):

Write a short answer to each question.

1. Where does space begin?

2. What object most strongly affects the space environment?

3. What is the star closest to Earth? The second closest star?

4. List and describe the Sun's two forms of energy output.

5. What are solar flares? How are they different from the solar wind?

Chapter 3 The Space Environment

Section 3.2. The Space Environment and Spacecraft

(Homework Problems: A1; E1-E5)

A. Define, Describe, or Identify (Vocabulary):

1. Astrodynamics

2. Atmospheric density

3. Atmospheric pressure

4. Atomic oxygen

5. Bow shock

6. Cold welding

7. Conduction

8. Contact forces

9. Convection

10. Drag

11. Galactic cosmic rays (GCRs)

12. Magnetopause

13. Magnetosphere

14. Magnetotail

15. Out-gassing

16. Oxidation

17. Ozone

18. Photon

19. Radiation

20. Shock front

21. Single event phenomenon (SEP)

22. Solar cells

23. Solar pressure

24. Spacecraft charging

25. Sputtering

26. Van Allen radiation belts

B. Fill in the Blanks:

Fill in the blank with the word or words necessary to complete the statement.

1. In low-Earth orbit, the pull of gravity is still _____% of what it is on Earth's surface.

2. The atmosphere continues to exert drag on orbiting spacecraft up to an altitude of about _____ kilometers.

3. A good space lubricant that doesn't evaporate or change characteristics in a vacuum is _____.

4. Tracking harmful space debris is the job of the _____ _____ _____ _____ _____ in Colorado.

5. When exposed to thermal (infrared) radiation, a spacecraft can _____.

6. Earth's magnetic field traps _____ _____ and protects us from their harmful effects.

C. Multiple Choice:

Circle the letter that correctly answers the question or completes the statement.

1. Which of the following is <u>not</u> a hazard of space?

    a. Gravity

    b. Atmosphere

    c. Vacuum

    d. Noise

2. We experience _____ on Earth when we jump off a diving board.

    a. space flight

    b. free-fall

    c. disorientation

    d. zero gravity

3. In very low orbits, atmospheric drag pulls spacecraft back to Earth in just a few
    _____ or _____.

    a. years, more

    b. months, years

    c. weeks, months

    d. days, weeks

4. NASA's Long Duration Exposure Facility tested the harmful effects of
    _____ _____ (and other hazards) on various spacecraft
    surfaces.

    a. atomic oxygen

    b. atomic hydrogen

    c. spacecraft rotation

    d. magnetic fields

5. Because of cold welding, spacecraft designers try to avoid _____
    _____.

    a. aluminum parts

    b. moving parts

    c. heat conduction

    d. hard vacuums

6. A paint flake in orbit has more energy than a _____ _____
    on Earth.

    a. speeding locomotive

    b. race car

    c. rifle bullet

    d. fighter jet

D. Matching:

Match the item in Column A with the description in Column B. You may use an item from Column B only once, but you won't use all of them.

Column A

1. Astronauts in orbit _____
2. Space Shuttle re-entry _____
3. Bake a spacecraft _____
4. CERISE _____
5. Graveyard orbits _____
6. Ultraviolet radiation _____
7. Aurora Borealis _____

Column B

a. Prevents manmade debris hazard
b. Charged particle interaction with atmospheric gases
c. Degrades spacecraft surfaces
d. First spacecraft confirmed hit by junk
e. Protects against outgassing
f. Expanding space debris
g. Protects spacecraft inhabitants
h. Experience free-fall
i. Force of drag slows it

E. True/False:

Place a **T** in the blank if the statement is true, and an **F** in the blank if it is false.

_____ 1. The free-fall environment in space offers many opportunities for special manufacturing processes.

_____ 2. As a rocket climbs through the atmosphere, it experiences decreasing atmospheric density but increasing atmospheric pressure.

_____ 3. Among atomic oxygen (O), normal oxygen (O_2), and ozone (O_3), in the upper atmosphere, ozone is the most damaging to spacecraft surfaces.

_____ 4. Radiation is the primary means for moving heat into and out of a spacecraft.

_____ 5. If two spacecraft collided in space, the resulting debris cloud would greatly increase the probability of damage to other spacecraft.

F. Shorts Answer (Things to Think About):

Write a short answer to each question.

1. List the six major hazards to spacecraft in the space environment.

2. Why are astronauts in space not in "zero gravity"? Why is free-fall a better description of the gravity environment?

3. How do the density and pressure of Earth's atmosphere change with altitude?

4. What is atmospheric drag?

5. What is atomic oxygen? How can it affect spacecraft?

6. What are the biggest problems in the vacuum of space?

7. Describe the possible hazards to spacecraft from micrometeoroids and space junk.

8. Describe what protects the Earth from the effects of solar and cosmic charged particles.

9. What are Galactic Cosmic Rays?

10. What are the Van Allen radiation belts and what do they contain?

11. Describe the possible harmful effects on spacecraft from charged particles.

Chapter 3 The Space Environment

Section 3.3. Living and Working in Space

(Homework Problems: B2, B5, C1-C5)

A. Define, Describe, or Identify (Vocabulary):

1. Acute dosages

2. Edema

3. Fluid shift

B. Fill in the Blanks:

Fill in the blank with the word or words necessary to complete the statement.

1. One effect of extra fluid in the upper body during free-fall is a decrease in
_____ _____ _____ production.

2. Most astronauts experience _____ _____ during the first
few days in space, until their senses adjust to free-fall.

3. Brisk _____ offers some promise in preventing long-term
weakening of astronaut muscles while they are in orbit.

4. NASA sets astronaut radiation dosage _____.

5.   Being _____ and away from _____ contribute to mental and
emotional stresses on space missions.

C. Multiple Choice:

Circle the letter that correctly answers the question or completes the statement.

1. Which of the following is <u>not</u> a possibly harmful change to the human body in free-fall?

   a. Fluid shift

   b. Motion sickness

   c. Lengthening of the spinal column

   d. Reduced load on the weight-bearing tissues

2. _____ loss and the related bone weakness may be progressive for astronauts in orbit.

   a. Conditioning

   b. Fluid

   c. Mass

   d. Calcium

3. For long interplanetary space missions, some scientists suggest that astronauts have _____ _____ to maintain the load on weight-bearing bones and muscles.

   a. artificial gravity

   b. extra exercise

   c. extreme vitamins

   d. heavy duties

4. People suffer more when exposed to a _____ amount of radiation in a _____ time.

   a. small, short

   b. large, short

   c. small, long

   d. small, medium

5. To protect astronauts from solar flares, long missions may need

   _____ _____.

   a. high speed

   b. extra doctors

   c. stronger medicine

   d. storm shelters

D. Matching:

Match the item in Column A with its description in Column B. You may use an item from Column B only once, but you won't use all of them.

Column A	*Column B*
1. Fluid shift ____	a. When bedridden or in free-fall
2. Fragile bones ____	b. Avoid space walks here
3. Muscles get smaller and weaker ____	c. After 1-2 years in microgravity
4. Galactic cosmic rays ____	d. Hard on fast reproducing cells
5. South Atlantic Anomaly ____	e. Hard to shield astronauts because of high energy
	f. Dizziness
	g. Causes edema of the face

E. True/False:

Place a **T** in the blank if the statement is true, and an **F** in the blank if it is false.

_____ 1. In free-fall, body fluids no longer pool in our legs.

_____ 2. Astronauts' hearts must work harder in orbit to maintain blood pressure.

_____ 3. Scientists have not found a cure for the changes in astronauts' bones while in orbit.

_____ 4. In space, when astronauts get too tired, their performance decreases, which may endanger the mission.

_____ 5. Because of the excitement of space flight, astronaut crews always get along well during space missions.

F. Short Answers (Things to Think About):

Write a short answer to each question.

1. List and describe the three changes to the human body during free-fall?

2. How might exposure to radiation and charged particles affect humans in the short term? In the long term?

3. How do long space flights affect astronauts mentally and emotionally?

G. List or Describe:

1. As a spacecraft designer for a manned mission to Mars, you must protect the crew from the space environment. Compile a list of all the potential hazards they may face during this multi-year mission and discuss how you plan to deal with them.

UNIT 2: Orbits and Trajectories

Chapter 4 Understanding Orbits

Section 4.1. Orbital Motion

(Homework Problems: B1-B2, C3, E1-E4)

A. Define, Describe, or Identify (Vocabulary):

1. Acceleration due to gravity

2. Coordinate system

3. Equation of motion

4. Error analysis

5. Initial conditions

6. Simplifying assumptions

7. Testing the model

B. Fill in the Blanks:

Fill in the blank with the word or words necessary to complete the statement.

1. If two baseball players each release a baseball—one throws horizontally at 100 kilometers per hour and one drops the ball vertically from the same height—which will hit the ground (assuming level ground) first? _____.

2. Earth's round shape causes its surface to drop _____ meters vertically for every _____ kilometers horizontally.

3. If we throw an object at _____ kilometers per second, it's path would exactly match Earth's curve resulting in a path that looks like a circle, assuming no air drag.

4. To analyze an object's motion, we first define a _____ _____, so we can measure its path along each axis.

C. Multiple Choice:

Circle the letter that correctly answers the question or completes the statement.

1. Just above Earth's surface, an object thrown horizontally at 7.9 kilometers per second will continue around Earth at a _____ _____, assuming no air drag.

    a. constant height

    b. climbing attitude

    c. descending attitude

    d. slower speed

2. It's true that an object in orbit is literally _____ around Earth, but because of its horizontal speed it never quite _____ the ground.

    a. speeding, leaves

    b. falling, hits

    c. climbing, sees

    d. flying, approaches

3. To analyze all types of motion, we use a system called the Mission Analysis Process _____.

    a. satellite

    b. system

    c. checklist

    d. baseball

4. The second step in the Motion Analysis Process asks for a simple way of describing a spacecraft's motion—a (an) _____ _____ _____.

    a. level of understanding

    b. trial and error

    c. best guess method

    d. equation of motion

D. Matching:

Match the item in Column A with its description in Column B. You may use an item from Column B only once, but you won't use all of them.

Column A

1. Minimum speed to go around Earth ___
2. An object falls ____
3. Simplifying assumption ____
4. Initial conditions ____

Column B

a. Venus's gravity doesn't affect a baseball on Earth
b. Analyze differences between model and test cases
c. About 8 kilometers horizontally
d. Beginning speed and direction
e. Slower than 7.9 kilometers per second
f. 7.9 kilometers per second

E. True/False:

Place a **T** in the blank if the statement is true, and an **F** in the blank if it is false.

_____ 1. Near Earth's surface, gravity pulls on everything with a constant acceleration.

_____ 2. No matter how fast we throw an object horizontally, it still falls toward Earth at the same rate.

_____ 3. We choose a coordinate system before analyzing an object's motion.

_____ 4. If we assume that gravity is the only force on a spacecraft in orbit, then we made a bad assumption.

F. Short Answers (Things to Think About):

Write a short answer to each question.

1. Explain how an object's horizontal speed allows it to achieve orbit.

2. Explain how you could use the steps in the Motion Analysis Process checklist to analyze the motion of serving a volleyball.

Chapter 4 Understanding Orbits

Section 4.2. Newton's Laws

(Homework Problems: A1, A2, A6, A11, B1-B8)

A. Define, Describe, or Identify (Vocabulary):

1. Acceleration

2. Angular momentum

3. Angular velocity

4. Inertia

5. Linear momentum

6. Mass

7. Moment arm

8. Moment of inertia

9. Momentum

10. Square

11. Tangential speed

12. Universal Gravitational Constant

13. Weight

B. Fill in the Blanks:

Fill in the blank with the word or words necessary to complete the statement.

1. _____ _____ formed the basic laws of motion that revolutionized our understanding of the world.

2. An object at rest has a certain amount of _____ (represented by its mass) that must be overcome to move it.

3. A body continues in its state of rest, or of uniform motion in a _____ _____, unless compelled to change that state by forces impressed upon it. (Newton's First Law)

4. To calculate an object's linear momentum, we need to know its _____ and _____.

5. An object's angular momentum depends on its _____ _____ and its _____ _____ _____.

6. The time rate of change of an object's _____ equals the applied force. (Newton's Second Law)

7. If two ice skaters start at rest and the first one pushes against the second, they will both go backward – the first skater applied an action – pushing – and received an equal, but opposite reaction, thus demonstrating Newton's _____ _____.

8. An object twice as far away from Earth experiences _____ as much gravity as it originally had.

C. Multiple Choice:

Circle the letter that correctly answers the question or completes the statement.

1. Mass is _____.
    a. how much an object weighs plus the influence of gravity
    b. how much matter is in an object
    c. how much an object weighs
    d. how much an object resists changes in motion

2. A bowling ball rolling straight has this property because its mass is moving.

    a. Inertia

    b. Height

    c. Stuff

    d. Direction

3. A bullet fired at a target will fly in a (an) _____ _____ unless acted upon by an outside force.

    a. unknown path

    b. spiral path

    c. straight line

    d. curved path

4. A bulldozer speeding along at 1 kilometer per hour resists any change in its speed or direction because it has a large _____ _____.

    a. gasoline engine

    b. forward motion

    c. moving force

    d. linear momentum

5. A spinning toy top won't fall over when placed on a table because it has _____ _____.

    a. linear momentum

    b. angular momentum

    c. no momentum

    d. unknown powers

6. To change an object's momentum (linear or angular), we must apply a _____.

    a. resistance

    b. force

    c. grease

    d. color

7. Isaac Newton's Second Law says that if we apply a force to a mass, we will _____ it.

    a. accelerate

    b. damage

    c. topple

    d. turn

8. Newton's Law of Universal Gravitation says the force of gravity between two bodies is _____ _____.

    a. not related

    b. inversely proportional

    c. directly proportional

    d. always equal

D. Matching:

Match the item in Column A with its description in Column B. You may use an item from Column B only once, but you won't use all of them.

Column A	*Column B*
1. Newton's First Law ____	a. An object's resistance to spin
2. Newton's Second Law ____	b. Gravity is the only force on a spacecraft
3. Newton's Third Law ____	c. A body at rest stays at rest—inertia
4. Newton's Law of Universal Gravitation ____	d. Action-reaction
5. Moment of inertia ____	e. A net force causes an acceleration
	f. Force is inversely proportional to the square of the distance
	g. How much stuff it has

E. True/False:

Place a **T** in the blank if the statement is true, and an **F** in the blank if it is false.

_____ 1. Even though your mass doesn't change, you weigh more in Houston, TX (elevation 0 meters) than you do in Leadville, CO (elevation 3048 meters).

_____ 2. If we see an object not moving in a straight line, some force must be acting on it.

_____ 3. We use the natural shape of our left hand to describe the direction of a spinning object.

_____ 4. Acceleration tells us how fast an object's speed is changing.

F. Short Answer (Things to Think About):

Write a short answer to each question.

1. What three things does an object's mass tell you about the object?

2. An astronaut on the Moon drops a hammer and a feather from the same height at the same time. Describe what happens and why. Explain the difference if this experiment is done on Earth.

3. Describe how the backward force you feel when firing a rifle is the result of Newton's Third Law of Motion.

4. A rocket engine moves forward by putting out high-speed gas from the exhaust nozzle. Discuss the physical law that explains why this produces a force on the rocket.

Chapter 5 Maneuvering in Space

Section 5.1. Spacecraft Ground Tracks

(Homework Problems: A1-A6, C1-C5)

A. Define, Describe, or Identify (Vocabulary):

1. Geostationary orbit

2. Geosynchronous orbit

3. Great circle

4. Ground track

5. Orbital plane

6. Orbital trace

7. Orbital period

B. Fill in the Blanks:

Fill in the blank with the word or words necessary to complete the statement.

1. Many spacecraft _____ need to know what part of Earth their spacecraft is passing over.

2. A spacecraft goes _____ the way around Earth during each orbit.

3. Lines of _____ are not great circles because they don't slice through Earth's center.

4. If we stretch a globe so it's flat, spacecraft ground tracks look _____.

5. Orbital planes are _____ in space.

6. _____ orbits have a period of 24 hours and an inclination of 0°.

C. Multiple Choice:

Circle the letter that correctly answers the question or completes the statement.

1. _____ _____ satellites must be over an exact location to get the coverage they need.

    a. All orbiting

    b. Remote sensing

    c. No orbiting

    d. Ground track

2. Automobile drivers trace their route on a _____ by drawing a line.

    a. roadway

    b. highway

    c. roadmap

    d. path

3. All the way around Earth is about _____ kilometers.

    a. 10,000

    b. 25,000

    c. 30,000

    d. 40,000

4. The great circle on Earth with 0° latitude is called the _____.

    a. equator

    b. pole

    c. longitude

    d. orbit

5. Each ground track traces a path on Earth farther to the _____ than the previous one (for spacecraft with periods less than 24 hours).

    a. west

    b. east

    c. north

    d. south

D. Matching:

Match the term in Column A with its description in Column B. You may use items from Column B only once, but you won't use all of them.

Column A	*Column B*
1. Spacecraft's ground track ____	a. Travels 1600 kilometers per hour
2. Earth's spin on its axis ____	b. Line of longitude
3. Geosynchronous orbit ____	c. Path over Earth's surface
4. Great circle ____	d. Line of latitude
5. Geostationary orbit ____	e. Spacecraft stays over one point on the equator
	f. Once per day
	g. Takes about 24 hours to orbit the Earth

E. True/False:

Place a **T** in the blank if the statement is true, and an **F** in the blank if it is false.

_____ 1. We learn a lot about a spacecraft's orbit and mission by looking at its track along Earth's surface.

_____ 2. An airplane's ground track is usually straighter than an automobile's.

_____ 3. Not all orbital planes slice through Earth's center.

_____ 4. If you see a spacecraft overhead at night, it will be farther west on its next pass.

_____ 5. For a geosynchronous orbit, it's period matches Earth's rotation rate—24 hours.

F. Short Answers (Things to Think About):

Write a short answer to each question.

1. What type of ground track does a geostationary spacecraft have?

2. What type of period does a geostationary orbit have?

3. What is a great circle?

4. What is an orbital trace?

5. What is an orbital plane?

G. List or Describe:

1. Describe the motion of a spacecraft in its orbit compared with an observer on Earth, while it rotates.

Chapter 5 Maneuvering in Space

Section 5.2. Simple Orbit Changes

(Homework Problems: B1-B5, D1-D5, F3)

A. Define, Describe, or Identify (Vocabulary):

1. Hohmann Transfer

2. Kinetic energy

3. Potential energy

4. Rendezvous

5. Total energy

6. Transfer orbit

B. Fill in the Blanks:

Fill in the blank with the word or words necessary to complete the statement.

1. When going from one orbit to another, we keep things simple by saying the first and final orbits must be in the same _____.

2. The Gemini space program developed the procedures for _____ between two spacecraft in space.

3. When performing a Hohmann Transfer we change the initial _____ orbit into an orbit shaped like an _____.

4. For rocket scientists, saving energy means saving _____.

5. The _____ of a spacecraft in orbit about Earth depends only on the orbit's _____.

C. Multiple Choice:

Circle the letter that correctly answers the question or completes the statement.

1. When we maneuver a spacecraft, we have to worry about how much
   _____ it takes.

   a. space

   b. fuel

   c. money

   d. attention

2. The _____ _____ uses the least amount of fuel
   when transferring from one orbit to another.

   a. Hohmann Transfer

   b. slow transfer

   c. fast transfer

   d. Newton transfer

3. A spacecraft increases or decreases its velocity by firing _____
   _____.

   a. fire crackers

   b. gasoline engines

   c. rocket engines

   d. laser guns

4. When going from a lower orbit to a higher orbit, a spacecraft must
   _____ twice, but will be going _____ in the final orbit.

   a. accelerate, slower

   b. decelerate, faster

   c. accelerate, faster

   d. decelerate, slower

D. Matching:

Match the item in Column A with its description in Column B. You may use an item from Column B only once, but you won't use all of them.

Column A		*Column B*	
1. Gemini Program _____		a.	Fire rocket parallel to the direction of travel
2. Walter Hohmann _____		b.	Launched in the 1960s
3. Tangential velocity change _____		c.	Two spacecraft arrive at the same point in space
4. Kinetic energy _____		d.	Went to the Moon
5. Rendezvous _____		e.	Designed fuel-saving transfer orbits
		f.	A car has it due to it's velocity
		g.	Based on height above the ground

E. True/False:

Place a **T** in the blank if the statement is true, and an **F** in the blank if it is false.

_____ 1. Spacecraft never change orbits after they arrive in space.

_____ 2. To do a Hohmann Transfer a spacecraft starts in a circular orbit, changes to an elliptical transfer orbit, then changes again to a circular orbit.

_____ 3. To slow down a spacecraft tangentially, we must point the rocket against the direction of travel.

_____ 4. A spacecraft's orbit size determines its energy.

F. Short Answers (Things to Think About):

Write a short answer to each question.

1. Give an example in which we might want to move a satellite from one orbit to another.

2. Describe the process used in a Hohmann Transfer to go from a low-Earth orbit to a higher Earth orbit. How would this process change if you wanted to go from a higher orbit to a lower orbit?

3. When going from a smaller circular orbit to a larger one, why do we speed up twice but end up with a slower velocity in the final orbit?

4. What is an elliptical transfer orbit and how is it important for the Hohmann Transfer?

G. List or Describe:

1. What types of space missions use rendezvous?

Chapter 6 Interplanetary Travel

Section 6.1. Planning for Interplanetary Travel

(Homework Problems: A1-A3, B1-B7)

A. Define, Describe, or Identify (Vocabulary):

1. Conic sections

2. Ecliptic plane

3. Heliocentric

4. Heliocentric-ecliptic coordinate system

5. Hyperbolic trajectory

6. Patched-conic approximation

7. Sphere of influence (SOI)

B. Fill in the Blanks:

Fill in the blank with the word or words necessary to complete the statement.

1. When a spacecraft crosses a boundary into interplanetary space, Earth's gravitational pull lessens and the _____'s pull becomes the strongest force.

2. In choosing the basic plane of the Sun-centered coordinate system, we use the plane of _____'s orbit around the Sun.

3. For a trip from Earth to Mars, we must consider the gravitational force on our spacecraft from _____ central bodies.

4. In Region 1, the pull of the _____'s gravity is assumed to be the only force.

5. Individual pieces of a spacecraft's trajectory are called _____ _____.

6. A more massive planet has a longer _____ _____.

7. A spacecraft's _____ with respect to Earth isn't the same as its _____ with respect to the Sun.

C. Multiple Choice:

Circle the letter that correctly answers the question or completes the statement.

1. To plan a trip from Earth to Mars, we expand our point of view to include the _____ _____.

   a. United States

   b. whole world

   c. Earth's atmosphere

   d. solar system

2. When we were first learning about orbits, which of the following are conclusions we made to simplify the orbital motion problem?

   a. Only two bodies

   b. Only Earth's gravity

   c. Starlight affects an orbit

   d. a and b above

3. We can relate any trajectory from Earth to another planet to the _____-_____ coordinate system.

   a. geocentric-equatorial

   b. heliocentric-ecliptic

   c. heliocentric-equatorial

   d. solar-Venus

4. In theory a body's gravitational attraction reaches out to _____.

   a. space

   b. 1 million kilometers

   c. infinity

   d. Venus

5. The ultimate goal for the patched-conic approximation is to find the total
    _____ _____ to leave Earth orbit and get into orbit
    around another planet.

    a. energy change

    b. momentum change

    c. velocity change

    d. gravity change

D. Matching:

Match the item in Column A with its description in Column B. You may use an item from Column B only once, but you won't use all of them.

Column A	Column B
1. Divide and conquer _____	a. Region 1 in the patched-conic solution
2. Earth-centered _____	b. One of four bodies in interplanetary travel
3. Sun-centered _____	c. Gravity pull of target planet is assumed to be the only force
4. Sphere of influence _____	d. Interplanetary travel starts here
5. Region 3 _____	e. Velocity decrease
6. Interplanetary spacecraft _____	f. About 1,000,000 kilometers for Earth
	g. Patched-conic approximation method
	h. Circular-orbit velocity

E. True/False:

Place a **T** in the blank if the statement is true, and an **F** in the blank if it is false.

_____ 1. Newton's Law of Universal Gravitation says the force of gravity between two bodies is inversely proportional to the product of their two masses.

_____ 2. In the region where the Sun's gravity is strongest, the spacecraft's path is not a conic section.

_____ 3. The patched-conic approximation breaks the interplanetary trajectory into three separate regions.

_____ 4. The size of a sphere of influence depends on the planet's mass and how close the planet is to the Sun.

_____ 5. In solving the patched-conic approximation, we find only one velocity common to problems 1 and 2 and only one velocity common to problems 2 and 3.

F. Short Answers (Things to Think About):

Write a short answer to each question.

1. How do we define the heliocentric-ecliptic coordinate frame?

2. What does a planet's sphere of influence (SOI) represent?

3. What are the three regions used in the patched-conic approximation of an interplanetary trajectory?

G. List or Describe:

1. Do we need to launch interplanetary probes or can we learn enough about other planets through telescopes on the ground and in Earth orbit?

Chapter 6 Interplanetary Travel

Section 6.2. Gravity-assist Trajectories

(Homework Problems: A2-A3, D1-D5)

A. Define, Describe, or Identify (Vocabulary):

1. Gravity assist

2. Orbit cranking

3. Orbit pumping

B. Fill in the Blanks:

Fill in the blank with the word or words necessary to complete the statement.

1. If the Voyager missions had relied totally on _____ to steer between the planets, they would never have gotten off the ground.

2. The "sling shot" maneuver changes a spacecraft's velocity (in _____ and _____) with respect to the Sun.

3. The gravity of Jupiter _____ the Ulysses solar-polar satellite out of the ecliptic plane into an orbit around the Sun's poles.

4. To use the "sling shot" maneuver, a spacecraft enters a planet's _____ _____ _____, and then the planet pulls it in the direction of the planet's motion, increasing (or decreasing) its velocity relative to the Sun.

5. When a spacecraft passes in front of a planet, it's pulled in the _____ direction, slowing down the spacecraft and _____ its orbit with respect to the Sun.

C. Multiple Choice:

Circle the letter that correctly answers the question or completes the statement.

1. Often, we can't justify a mission that relies only on _____ to get the required velocity change.

    a. luck

    b. rockets

    c. assists

    d. money

2. A gravity-assist trajectory uses a planet's gravity and orbital _____ to "sling shot" a spacecraft.

    a. position

    b. rotation

    c. velocity

    d. timing

3. During a gravity-assisted velocity change, the spacecraft _____ velocity from the planet, causing it to speed up or slow down ever so slightly.

    a. adds

    b. subtracts

    c. returns

    d. steals

4. If a spacecraft passes behind a planet, the planet pulls it in the direction of the planet's motion, causing it to _____ velocity with respect to the Sun.

    a. lose

    b. drop

    c. maintain

    d. gain

5. The _____ spacecraft used gravity-assist flybys at several planets before leaving the solar system.

    a. Voyager

    b. Ulysses

    c. Galileo

    d. Shuttle

D. Matching:

Match the item in Column A with its description in Column B. You may use an item from Column B only once, but you won't use all of them.

Column A	*Column B*
1. Gravity-assist trajectory ____	a. Velocity magnitude change only
2. Pass behind the planet _____	b. Nearly free velocity change
3. Pass in front of the planet _____	c. Required for interplanetary travel
4. Orbit cranking _____	d. High risk to spacecraft systems
5. Orbit pumping _____	e. Velocity direction change only
	f. Increases velocity with respect to the Sun
	g. Decreases velocity with respect to the Sun

E. True/False:

Place a **T** in the blank if the statement is true, and an **F** in the blank if it is false.

_____ 1. NASA spacecraft have never used gravity-assist trajectories to send interplanetary spacecraft out of the solar system.

_____ 2. Gravity-assist trajectories often make the difference between possible and impossible missions.

_____ 3. Gravity-assist trajectories work best if the spacecraft stays outside the planet's sphere of influence.

_____ 4. After a gravity-assist flyby, a spacecraft has a different trajectory with respect to the Sun than before the flyby.

_____ 5. The spacecraft named Galileo flew to Jupiter using three gravity-assist flybys to gain enough velocity to finish its trip.

F. Short Answers (Things to Think About):

Write a short answer to each question.

1. Explain how we can use gravity assist to get "free velocity change" for interplanetary transfers.

2. Is change in velocity from a gravity assist really "free"?

3. Can a flyby of the Sun help us change a spacecraft's interplanetary trajectory?

Chapter 7 Ballistic Missiles and Getting into Orbit

Section 7.1. Intercontinental Ballistic Missiles (ICBMs)

(Homework Problems: A1-A3, C1-C5)

A. Define, Describe, or Identify (Vocabulary):

1. Anti-ballistic Missile Treaty (ABM Treaty)

2. Ballistics

3. Ballistic trajectories

4. Ellipse

5. Hyperbola

6. Inertial-guidance system

7. Intercontinental Ballistic Missiles (ICBMs)

8. Minuteman I and II

9. Minuteman III

10. Multiple independently targetable re-entry vehicles (MIRVs)

11. Parabola

12. Peacekeeper

B. Fill in the Blanks:

Fill in the blank with the word or words necessary to complete the statement.

1. Most of an ICBM's trajectory is _____ the atmosphere and we ignore all other forces except _____.

2. Intermediate-range ballistic missiles, short-range ballistic missiles, and the theater ballistic missiles differ mostly in _____ _____.

3. Many of the people who played key roles in the global space program also took part in developing _____.

4. The Minuteman ballistic missile was the first mass-produced system to use a computer built from _____ _____.

5. The first "third-generation" ICBM was the _____, which ended service in 2004 according to the SALT II Treaty.

6. In December 2001, President Bush gave Russia notice that the United States was _____ from the Anti-ballistic Missile Treaty.

C. Multiple Choice:

Circle the letter that correctly answers the question or completes the statement.

1. Which of the following is <u>not</u> traveling on a ballistic trajectory?

    a. Baseball hit into the air (neglecting air friction)

    b. ICBM after its rocket cuts off

    c. Bullet shot into the air (ignoring air friction)

    d. Bowling ball rolling down an alley

2. Which of the following are ballistic missile burnout conditions?

    a. Velocity

    b. Direction of flight

    c. Body length

    d. a and b above

3. Which of the following is <u>not</u> a ballistic missile?

    a. Atlas

    b. Minuteman

    c. Titan

    d. Zeus

4. Solid rocket motors are ideal for ICBMs because of their _____.

    a. rocket power

    b. quick response

    c. light weight

    d. smokeless exhaust

5. Something unusual about the Minuteman flight computer is that it used a rotating _____ _____ to store the computer program, because it was unaffected by radiation from nearby nuclear explosions.

    a. magnetic disk

    b. advanced sensor

    c. hard drive

    d. floppy drive

6. In 1976, Congress refused to fund a silo-based system for the Peacekeeper missile deployment, because it was too _____ to enemy attack.

    a. invisible

    b. vulnerable

    c. valuable

    d. hidden

7. The 1972 Anti-ballistic Missile Treaty stated that each nation may have only two ABM-deployment areas, restricted and located at least 1300 kilometers apart to prevent a (an) _____ ABM defense.

    a. local

    b. international

    c. simple

    d. nationwide

D. Matching:

Match the item in Column A with its description in Column B. You may use an item from Column B only once, but you won't use all of them.

Column A

1. Ballistics _____
2. Ballistic trajectories _____
3. High or low _____
4. Sapwood _____
5. Atlas B _____
6. Peacekeeper _____
7. ABM Treaty _____
8. National Missile Defense _____

Column B

a. Types of trajectories to the same target
b. Guided cruise missile
c. First U.S. ICBM
d. Originally called MX missile program
e. In force for 30 years
f. Protects against nuclear blackmail
g. Expanding global nuclear weapons
h. The study of projectile motion
i. Mostly outside Earth's atmosphere
j. World's first ICBM

E. True/False:

Place a **T** in the blank if the statement is true, and an **F** in the blank if it is false.

_____ 1. Bullets, bombs, rockets, and missiles all fly on ballistic paths, ignoring air resistance.

_____ 2. A ballistic missile is a missile with a set course that cannot be changed after the missile has burned its fuel and the laws of ballistics start governing its course.

_____ 3. An ICBM can reach its target on a high trajectory or the maximum range trajectory.

_____ 4. The U.S. decommissioned the Peacekeeper missile by 2004, because of the SALT II agreement.

_____ 5. The Peacekeeper missile entered service at Malmstrom AFB, Montana, in 1986.

_____ 6. The SALT I agreement made sure that neither side could ever think it could strike first without being struck back.

F. Short Answers (Things to Think About):

Write a short answer to each question.

1. Describe the science called ballistics and the paths that ballistic objects follow.

2. Why do modern ICBMs carry multiple warheads, called multiple independently targetable re-entry vehicles (MIRVs)?

3. What two new changes gave the Minuteman ICBM a long practical service life, possibly to 2025?

4. How did research on the Strategic Defense Initiative (SDI) in 1982 disturb the delicate balance between the U.S. and the USSR in the Anti-ballistic Missile (ABM) Treaty of 1972?

G. List or Describe:

1. With new countries developing nuclear weapons, do you think it was wise for the U.S. to withdraw from the ABM Treaty of 1972? Why?

2. Do you think we should continue to work toward the limited National Missile Defense and do research on the expanded, space-based systems? Why?

Chapter 7 Ballistic Missiles and Getting into Orbit

Section 7.2. Launch Windows and Times

(Homework Problems: A1, F2)

A. Define, Describe, or Identify (Vocabulary):

1. Apparent solar day

2. Greenwich Mean Time (GMT)

3. Launch window

4. Local sidereal time (LST)

5. Mean solar day

6. Right ascension of the ascending node

7. Sidereal day

8. Sidereal time

9. Solar time

10. Vernal equinox direction

B. Fill in the Blanks:

Fill in the blank with the word or words necessary to complete the statement.

1. The _____ _____ is the period of time when we can launch a spacecraft directly into a specific orbit from a give launch site.

2. When a launch site and an orbital plane _____ we have a launch window.

3. We can tell time just as easily in degrees as in hours if we use Earth as a giant _____.

4. The time since the vernal equinox passed over a local longitude is called _____ _____ time.

5. Earth must rotate on its axis slightly _____ than 360° to bring the Sun repeatedly over a given location.

6. A sidereal day is slightly _____ than a solar day.

C. Multiple Choice:

Circle the letter that correctly answers the question or completes the statement.

1. We can _____ launch a spacecraft into a parking orbit and maneuver it into its mission orbit.

    a. never

    b. seldom

    c. often

    d. always

2. A launch window normally covers a period of time during which a spacecraft can launch, this period of time is usually a few _____ or even _____ around an exact time.

    a. minutes, hours

    b. hours, days

    c. days, weeks

    d. week, months

3. Earth's rotation under the spacecraft's intended orbit is _____.

    a. unusual

    b. uneven

    c. periodic

    d. irregular

4. Because Earth's orbit around the Sun is slightly elliptical, the _____ _____ day's length varies through the year.

    a. usual sidereal

    b. mean solar

    c. apparent solar

    d. Greenwich solar

5. The Prime Meridian (0° longitude) runs through which town?

    a. New York, New York

    b. Washington, DC

    c. Frankfort, Germany

    d. Greenwich, England

6. Earth rotates at a very steady _____° per hour (approximate).

    a. 1

    b. 10

    c. 15

    d. 20

7. For sidereal time, it makes sense to define time as a (an) _____, because we're dealing with Earth's rotation.

    a. hour

    b. rate

    c. angle

    d. spin

8. Because Earth rotates more than 360° in a solar day, stars such as the Aquarius constellation appear _____ minutes earlier than the previous night.

    a. 2

    b. 4

    c. 8

    d. 12

D. Matching:

Match the item in Column A with its description in Column B. You may use an item from Column B only once, but you won't use all of them

Column A	*Column B*
1. Launch window _____	a. 24 solar hours
2. Vernal equinox _____	b. Time since vernal equinox was overhead
3. Sundial _____	c. 23 solar hours, 56 solar minutes, 4 solar seconds
4. Mean solar day _____	d. Span about 15° of longitude
5. Greenwich Mean Time, GMT ____	e. 15° per hour
6. Sidereal day _____	f. Period of time when we can push the launch button
7. Local sidereal time _____	g. Local solar time at Prime Meridian
8. Time zones _____	h. Measure sidereal time from it
	i. Marked time between Sun's passages
	j. Right ascension of the ascending node

E. True/False:

Place a **T** in the blank if the statement is true, and an **F** in the blank if it is false.

_____ 1. A launch site comes under a polar orbit twice a day.

_____ 2. To avoid confusion across time zones, we choose the London meridian as an international reference point.

_____ 3. For sidereal time it makes sense to define "time" as an angle because we're dealing with Earth's rotation.

_____ 4. When a launch site and an orbital plane intersect, we have a launch window and can launch directly into that orbit.

_____ 5. Three o'clock pm (1500 hours) is the same as 150° for calculating a launch window.

F. Short Answers (Things to Think About):

Write a short answer to each question.

1. What is a launch window?

2. How do mission planners specify a desired orbit so a spacecraft can do its mission?

3. What is local sidereal time (LST)? Draw a diagram to illustrate your answer. What does "sidereal" mean?

4. Why do we use sidereal rather than solar time for figuring launch windows?

5. What is the difference between solar and sidereal time? Draw a diagram to illustrate which is longer and why.

6. How does local sidereal time (LST) change as Earth rotates? How does right ascension of the ascending node change as Earth rotates?

7. If LST is 45° what is it in hours, minutes and seconds? Draw a diagram to illustrate this time.

8. If your current location has rotated 50° past the vernal equinox direction, what is your LST in hours, minutes, and seconds?

Chapter 8 Returning from Space: Re-entry

Section 8.1. Understanding Re-entry Motion

(Homework Problems: A1, A9-A10, B1-B7)

A. Define, Describe, or Identify (Vocabulary):

1. Ballistic coefficient (BC)

2. Coefficient of drag

3. Deceleration

4. Drag

5. Inverse relationship

6. Lift

7. Point mass

8. Re-entry coordinate system

9. Re-entry corridor

10. Re-entry flight-path angle

B. Fill in the Blanks:

Fill in the blank with the word or words necessary to complete the statement.

1. A vehicle's structure and payload limit the maximum _____it can withstand.

2. A re-entering vehicle that doesn't slow down enough may actually _____ off the atmosphere and back into _____.

3. The Space Shuttle has enough energy during re-entry to _____the average home in Colorado for 41 years.

4. The Space Shuttle must land on a runway only _____ meters wide.

5. The origin of the re-entry coordinate system is the vehicle's _____ _____ _____ at the start of re-entry.

6. For re-entry problems, the force of _____ is the main force acting on a vehicle.

7. An object with a low ballistic coefficient (BC) slows down _____ than an object with a high BC.

C. Multiple Choice:

Circle the letter that correctly answers the question or completes the statement.

1. Which of the following is <u>not</u> a competing requirement for re-entry design?
   a. Heating
   b. Deceleration
   c. Velocity
   d. Accuracy

2. Humans can withstand acceleration no higher than _____ g's for just a few minutes during re-entry.
   a. 3
   b. 6
   c. 9
   d. 12

3. The Apollo missions required the capsules to land in _____ areas of the Pacific Ocean.

    a. accurate

    b. insignificant

    c. critical

    d. large

4. If a re-entering vehicle strays below the re-entry corridor, it may _____ _____ _____.

    a. experience high drag

    b. slow down rapidly

    c. heat too quickly

    d. all of the above

5. The basic plane for the re-entry coordinate system is the _____ _____ plane.

    a. Earth's equatorial

    b. local horizontal

    c. vehicle's orbital

    d. Sun's ecliptic

6. During re-entry, a vehicle's flight-path angle below the horizon is _____.

    a. zero

    b. negative

    c. positive

    d. constant

7. If we know a meteor's mass and the _____ force acting on it, Newton's Second Law tells us how to find its _____.

    a. small, deceleration

    b. drag, deceleration

    c. equal, acceleration

    d. main, acceleration

8. A blunt object, such as an Apollo capsule, re-entering Earth's atmosphere has a _____ ballistic coefficient and thus, slows more _____ than a streamlined object.

    a. high, rapidly

    b. high, slowly

    c. low, rapidly

    d. low, slowly

D. Matching:

Match the item in Column A with its description in Column B. You may use an item from Column B only once, but you won't use all of them.

Column A	*Column B*
1. g's _____	a. Apollo missions used a shallow one
2. Air friction _____	b. Main direction is down
3. Re-entry coordinate frame _____	c. Force perpendicular to re-entry motion
4. ICBM Re-entry vehicle _____	d. Acceleration or deceleration measurement
5. Re-entry angle _____	e. Turns kinetic energy into heat
6. Light, blunt vehicle _____	f. Outside the re-entry corridor
7. Meteor _____	g. Low ballistic coefficient
	h. High accuracy requirement
	i. Most burn up before hitting Earth

E. True/False:

Place a **T** in the blank if the statement is true, and an **F** in the blank if it is false.

_____ 1. During re-entry, the Space Shuttle converts vast amounts of kinetic and potential energy into electrical energy.

_____ 2. If a re-entry capsule misses the re-entry corridor too high, it may skip back into space, but with too little velocity to stay in orbit.

_____ 3. The Space Shuttle's lift is small when compared to drag.

_____ 4. Lower ballistic coefficient values mean lower drag on re-entering vehicles.

_____ 5. Most meteors enter the atmosphere at extremely high speed and burn up long before they can hit Earth.

F. Short Answers (Things to Think About):

Write a short answer to each question.

1. What are the three competing re-entry requirements?

2. Where does all the heat produced during re-entry come from?

3. Why would increasing the ability of a re-entry vehicle to withstand higher g forces not necessarily increase the maximum deceleration requirement for the mission?

4. What is the re-entry corridor? Define its upper and lower boundaries.

5. What are the potential forces on a re-entry vehicle? What is the dominant force during re-entry? Why?

6. Define ballistic coefficient (BC). Describe how a blunt shape affects how a body will slow down due to drag. Describe how a streamlined shape affects the way a body will slow due to drag.

UNIT 3: Spacecraft and Launch Vehicles

Chapter 9 Space Systems Engineering

Section 9.1. Space Mission Design

(Homework Problems: A4, A13; D1-D9)

A. Define, Describe, or Identify (Vocabulary):

1. Acceptable operating ranges

2. Attitude and orbit control subsystem (AOCS)

3. Attitude-control budget

4. Communication and data-handling subsystem (CDHS)

5. Data budgets

6. Design-for-manufacturing principles

7. Design-to-cost

8. Environmental control and life-support subsystem (ECLSS)

9. Link budget

10. Operations concept

11. Orbital-control budget

12. Performance budget

13. Propellant budget

14. Subsystem performance budget

15. Systems engineering

B. Fill in the Blanks:

Fill in the blank with the word or words necessary to complete the statement.

1. All design problems begin with a _____.

2. We begin systems engineering by defining the top-level _____ requirements and constraints.

3. Mission requirements give us a way to _____ our performance by comparing where we are with where we want to go.

4. To help us define space mission requirements, we begin by creating a _____ _____.

5. An example mission statement for FireSat is to _____ and _____ forest fires worldwide and provide timely notification to users.

6. Mission constraints are _____ on what we can do.

7. Balanced against cost and schedule is _____.

8. While mission requirements focus on the big picture, the systems requirements focus on each element of the _____ _____.

9. For the FireSat mission, the payload may detect _____ or _____ from the forest fires.

10. Designers use the _____ _____ to re-evaluate the requirements based on new information that affects the current design.

11. _____ and _____ design is the final phase of space systems engineering.

12. The number and type of _____ we choose, and how they work together to form the payload, determine how we design the rest of the _____ to support it.

13. A spacecraft has to have the right _____ or orientation to point cameras and antennas at targets on Earth.

14. _____ control is always critical to keep payloads working normally.

15. During design, changes to one subsystem lead to _____ in another, so this makes the design process _____.

C. Multiple Choice:

Circle the letter that correctly answers the question or completes the statement.

1. Before we begin solving a problem, we want to know we're solving the _____ problem.

    a. best

    b. right

    c. neighbor's

    d. important

2. The first and most important step in systems engineering is to define the _____ _____.

    a. budget levels

    b. user requests

    c. mission requirements

    d. engineering team

3. Requirements must be _____ and _____.

    a. clear, simple

    b. short, sweet

    c. long, detailed

    d. thorough, entertaining

4. Which of the following groups are users for the FireSat mission data?

    a. U.S. Forest Service

    b. National agencies that fight forest fires

    c. International agencies that fight forest fires

    d. All of the above

5. A system design with the best technical solution offering the greatest performance may be _____ and _____ consuming.

    a. quick, budget

    b. cheap, time

    c. wrong, budget

    d. expensive, time

6. Which of the following might characterize the subject of a mission?

    a. Shape

    b. Temperature

    c. Frequency

    d. All of the above

7. Which of the following is not a characteristic of a forest fire that a sensor on FireSat might detect from space?

    a. Heat

    b. Light

    c. Shape

    d. Smoke

8. The spacecraft _____ exists just to support the payload.

    a. camera

    b. bus

    c. transmitter

    d. shape

9. The size and complexity of onboard data handling systems depend on the _____ of commands and data received, stored, processed, and transmitted, and how much the vehicle is built to operate on its own.

    a. amount

    b. type

    c. level

    d. process

10. A spacecraft's structure must be sturdy enough to handle all the high _____ and hold all the other _____ in place.

    a. pressure, panels

    b. temperature, pieces

    c. attention, parts

    d. loads, subsystems

11. Too often, first designs meet mission requirements but are difficult or impossible to _____.

    a. build

    b. launch

    c. transport

    d. lift

12. To help make design decisions, mission planners and systems engineers have a lot of _____ and _____ tools in their toolkit.

    a. space, electronic

    b. timely, effective

    c. design, analysis

    d. electrical, mechanical

13. Design teams can never achieve a _____ design, so at some point they must decide to quit designing at some point.

    a. simple

    b. perfect

    c. cheap

    d. safe

D. Matching:

Match the item in Column A with its description in Column B. You may use an item from Column B only once, but you won't use all of them.

	Column A		*Column B*
1.	Mission objective _____	a.	How all mission elements fit together
2.	Mission users _____	b.	Data speed and storage capabilities
3.	Operations concept _____	c.	Forest fires
4.	Spacecraft _____	d.	Create thrust needed to get spacecraft into orbit
5.	Mission constraint _____	e.	Why we do the mission
6.	FireSat mission subject _____	f.	Consists of a bus and payload
7.	Data budget _____	g.	Benefit from and use the information
8.	Large rockets on launch vehicles _____	h.	Forces us to compare our design to mission requirements
9.	Validation loop _____	i.	Produces electrical power
		j.	Limits what can be done
		k.	Derive payload requirements

E. True/False:

Place a **T** in the blank if the statement is true, and an **F** in the blank if it is false.

_____ 1. Requirements communicate what we need to others and to ourselves.

_____ 2. Budget constraints have become one of the biggest drivers of modern space missions.

_____ 3. A spacecraft's electrical power system typically carries on board its own energy source.

_____ 4. The spacecraft bus performs all the necessary housekeeping to keep the payload healthy and safe.

_____ 5. Designers must ensure their design is perfect before sending it to the technician who will make it.

F. Short Answers (Things to Think About):

Write a short answer to each question.

1. Describe the systems-engineering process and explain how it could be applied to an every day project.

2. What three things does the mission statement tell us?

3. What is the subject of a mission? How does the subject relate to the payload design?

4. Describe the mission objective and operations concept for our proposed FireSat. Why are these two things so important to overall mission design?

5. What is the subject of the proposed FireSat mission?

6. Describe the steps in space-systems engineering and relate them to the FireSat mission.

7. List the parts of the spacecraft bus and describe functions for each one.

8. Describe what happens during beginning spacecraft design. What are the key concerns for each subsystem? Why is this a repetitive process?

Chapter 10 Space-vehicle Control Systems

Section 10.1. Control Systems

(Homework Problems: A1, A6, A11, B1-B5)

A. Define, Describe, or Identify (Vocabulary):

1. Actuator

2. Block diagram

3. Closed-loop control system

4. Control systems

5. Controller

6. Feedback control system

7. Open-loop control system

8. Plant

9. Plant model

10. Sensor

11. Signals

12. System

B. Fill in the Blanks:

Fill in the blank with the word or words necessary to complete the statement.

1. Systems have _____ and _____, and a process in between.

2. Putting logs on a fire to heat a home is an example of a (an) _____-
   _____ control system.

3. The first step in a modern home heating-control system is to measure the current
   _____ in the house.

4. Closed-loop control systems are extremely useful because they can make a system
   do what we want regardless of random _____ inputs.

5. To support the payload, each subsystem in a spacecraft bus needs to
   _____ something.

C. Multiple Choice:

Circle the letter that correctly answers the question or completes the statement.

1. In an open-loop control system we can't adjust the _____ based on what's actually happening.

    a. outputs

    b. plant

    c. inputs

    d. feedback

2. The brain of a closed-loop control system decides whether to _____ _____ the actuator.

    a. turn on

    b. turn off

    c. reverse operate

    d. a or b above

3. Which of the following is <u>not</u> a basic task for a control system?

    a. Understand

    b. Observe

    c. Decide

    d. Direct

4. Controlling a spacecraft's _____ _____ is the job of the attitude and orbit control subsystem.

    a. angular momentum

    b. power level

    c. internal environment

    d. heat input

5. Which of the following are parts of a remote-sensing payload that may require closed-loop control?

    a. Exposure

    b. Aperture settings

    c. Imaging time and duration

    d. All of the above

D. Matching:

Match the item in Column A with its description in Column B. You may use an item from Column B only once, but you won't use all of them.

Column A	*Column B*
1. System _____	a. Leaving logs on a fire while we sleep
2. Block diagram _____	b. Random environmental inputs
3. Open-loop system _____	c. Controlled by the electrical power subsystem
4. Thermostat _____	d. Provided by the propulsion subsystem
5. Decide what to do _____	e. Turns inputs into outputs
6. Spacecraft power _____	f. Manages data storage and transmission
7. Rocket thrust _____	g. The job of the controller
	h. Boxes are components
	i. Controller for a closed-loop heating system

E. True/False:

Place a **T** in the blank if the statement is true, and an **F** in the blank if it is false.

_____ 1. In a modern home heating system, the house is the plant.

_____ 2. In a block diagram of a closed-loop control system we use a line to show the input feedback that adjusts the output.

_____ 3. In a propulsion control system, we control temperature and pressure to provide rocket thrust.

_____ 4. The human body systems run automatically, so we have no control systems.

_____ 5. An example of a random environmental input could be wind leaking in through a window of a house.

F. Short Answers (Things to Think About):

Write a short answer to each question.

1. What are block diagrams and why are they useful?

2. Define the four basic steps in control. Apply them to some everyday process such as hitting a baseball with a bat.

3. What is a plant model? What is the plant model for the baseball and bat example?

4. How do spacecraft use control?

5. What do sensors do in a control system? What sensors do you use to hit a baseball with a bat?

6. Draw a block diagram for the baseball-and-bat system. You are the controller and the bat is the actuator.

G. List or Describe

1. List a few open-loop control systems that we use regularly. What mechanism turns them on and off?

2. Will we ever produce a system that is totally independent of human influence? Why or why not?

Chapter 11 Spacecraft Subsystems

Section 11.1. Environmental Control and Life-support Subsystem (ECLSS)

(Homework Problems: A5, D1-D7, F11)

A. Define, Describe, or Identify (Vocabulary):

1. Absorptivity

2. Active thermal control

3. Albedo

4. Conductor

5. Dewar flasks

6. Emissivity

7. Flash evaporator

8. Heat pipes

9. Intimate-contact devices

10. Latent heat of fusion

11. Latent heat of vaporization

12. Life-support budget

13. Partial pressure

14. Passive thermal control

15. Radiation

16. Radiators

17. Reflectivity

18. Thermal equilibrium

19. Thermal node

20. Thermodynamics

21. Transmissivity

B. Fill in the Blanks:

Fill in the blank with the word or words necessary to complete the statement.

1.   Providing a livable environment in the harshness of space is the function of the

_____ _____ _____

_____ _____ _____ (ECLSS).

2.   Typically, the biggest problem for spacecraft thermal control is
_____ heat.

3.   Near Earth, the biggest source of heat for orbiting spacecraft is the
_____, because no _____ absorbs the radiant energy.

4.   The Stefan-Boltzmann relationship says that the energy emitted by an object
depends on its _____ and its ability to _____ or give
off heat.

5.   If we heat water on the stove, the hottest it gets is _____° Celsius.

6.   To remove heat from a hot component some spacecraft use _____
_____ that vaporizes and has a low melting point.

7.   Our bodies use _____to burn other chemicals as part of our metabolism.

8.   For Space Shuttle missions, tanks hold _____ oxygen and
_____ nitrogen.

9.   Besides for drinking, astronauts need water to prepare and _____
food, for bathing and _____ and for doing _____
and _____ clothes.

10. On the Space Shuttle, canisters containing _____ and
_____ _____ filter the air.

11. For long-term space missions, we need to establish a _____ system
that can retrieve and _____ water and other waste.

C. Multiple Choice:

Circle the letter that correctly answers the question or completes the statement.

1. To maintain a spacecraft's thermal equilibrium, the ECLSS must balance which of the following?

    a. Inputs

    b. Outputs

    c. Heat produced internally

    d. All of the above

2. Which of the following is <u>not</u> a source of heat for orbiting spacecraft?

    a. Sun

    b. Moon

    c. Earth

    d. Internal sources

3. Some Russian satellites rely on forced _____ to cool their spacecraft electronics.

    a. conduction

    b. convection

    c. radiation

    d. damper

4. When radiation strikes a surface, the energy will do which of the following?

    a. Reflect

    b. Absorb

    c. Transmit

    d. All of the above

5. _____ thermal control uses working fluids, heaters, pumps and other devices to move and eject heat.

    a. Passive

    b. Active

    c. External

    d. Recycled

6. A simple way to balance the hot (Sun) side and the cold (space) side of a spacecraft is to _____ it.

    a. rotate

    b. cool

    c. shade

    d. coat

7. Which of the following is <u>not</u> a human necessity for the life-support subsystem to provide?

    a. Oxygen

    b. Water

    c. Comfort

    d. Food

8. Typical astronauts (70 kilogram) need at least _____ calories a day to maintain their weight.

    a. 1150

    b. 1560

    c. 1972

    d. 2819

9. The Skylab orbiting laboratory was the first U.S. space system to use a free-fall _____ for waste management.

    a. bathroom

    b. trash bag

    c. sink

    d. toilet

10. To form the life-support budget, engineers multiply the daily human _____ by the number of astronauts and the total mission _____.

    a. waste, mass

    b. requirements, duration

    c. intake, requirements

    d. metabolism, consumption

D. Matching:

Match the item in Column A with its description in Column B. You may use an item from Column B only once, but you won't use all of them.

Column A	*Column B*
1. Infrared sensors ____	a. Solid medium passes heat
2. Albedo ____	b. Reflected solar energy from Earth
3. Earthshine ____	c. Hot-cold, hot-cold
4. Home insulation ____	d. Space windows for emitting heat
5. Absorptivity ____	e. Kapton™ layers for thermal control
6. Space blankets ____	f. Temperature requirement is about 70 Kelvin
7. Radiators ____	g. Ability to soak up radiation
8. Thermal cycling tests ____	h. Stops heat conduction through walls
	i. Emitted energy from Earth
	j. Must sum to equal 1

E. True/False:

Place a **T** in the blank if the statement is true, and an **F** in the blank if it is false.

_____ 1. If more heat leaves a spacecraft than goes in, then it begins to cool.

_____ 2. The nice thing about a passive thermal control system is that once it gets going, it doesn't need any other control inputs.

_____ 3. Shuttle astronauts must breathe pure oxygen for three to four hours before a space walk.

_____ 4. As a minimum, humans drink about four liters of water a day.

_____ 5. Without natural gravity, astronauts use artificial gravity to remove human waste in space.

_____ 6. Grueling thermal-vacuum tests simulate the space environment to certify a spacecraft's ECLSS is ready to fly.

F. Short Answers (Things to Think About):

Write a short answer to each question.

1. What two main things does a spacecraft's environmental control and life-support subsystem do?

2. Define thermal equilibrium.

3. Describe the potential sources of heat for a spacecraft.

4. Describe the three mechanisms of heat transfer. Give examples of each from everyday life.

5. Describe the difference between reflectivity, transmissivity, absorptivity, and emissivity.

6. What is the difference between active and passive thermal control?

7. List the ways a spacecraft can transfer heat internally.

8. Discuss ways a spacecraft can eject heat.

9. Cars have "radiators," but do they really radiate? Explain.

10. How does multi-layer insulation protect a spacecraft from external heat sources?

11. Define latent heat of fusion and describe how we can use this principle onboard a spacecraft.

12. List the inputs and outputs of the human "system."

13. Why do Shuttle crews reduce the cabin pressure 12 hours before an Extra Vehicular Activity?

14. What things go into the life-support budget for a crewed space mission?

15. Discuss analysis and testing issues for spacecraft's thermal-control subsystems.

G. List or Describe:

1. Does it seem reasonable to design a completely regenerable life-support system, where all human waste is recycled for future use? Why?

Chapter 12 Rockets and Launch Vehicles

Section 12.1. Rocket Science

(Homework Problems: A1-A4, A8, A12, A15-A17, A20, B2-B7)

A. Define, Describe, or Identify (Vocabulary):

1. Bernoulli Principle

2. Charge

3. Cold-gas rocket

4. Effective exhaust velocity

5. Electric field

6. Electrical potential

7. Electrodynamic energy

8. Electrodynamic rocket

9. Electrostatic force

10. Expansion ratio

11. Ideal rocket equation

12. Impulse

13. Impulse bits

14. Ion

15. Mass flow rate

16. Molecular mass

17. Nozzles

18. Power

19. Propellant

20. Specific impulse

21. Thermodynamic energy

22. Thermodynamic rocket

23. Throat

24. Thrust

25. Total impulse

B. Fill in the Blanks:

Fill in the blank with the word or words necessary to complete the statement.

1. A launch vehicle needs a large _____ _____ to get from Earth's surface into orbit.

2. A rocket ejects mass at high speed in one _____, so a vehicle can go in the other.

3. Without an outside force, linear momentum is always _____.

4. Specific impulse tells us the _____, in terms of the _____ mass, needed to produce a given _____ on a rocket.

5. The ideal rocket equation tells us the higher the _____ _____, the more _____ _____ can be delivered for a given mass of propellant used.

6. The first step in producing thrust in a rocket engine is to _____ energy into the _____ in some form.

7. A propellant can produce heat through a chemical reaction or from _____ sources.

8. The _____ Principle describes how rocket nozzles convert low-speed gases in the converging section into supersonic gases in the nozzle.

9. As we increase a combustion chamber's temperature, we increase a rocket engine's _____, measured by specific impulse.

10. _____ energy drives trains and produces electricity in power plants.

11. We get a higher specific impulse in an electrodynamic rocket by using a stronger _____ _____.

C. Multiple Choice:

Circle the letter that correctly answers the question or completes the statement.

1. Which of the following is (are) uses for a spacecraft's propulsion subsystem?

    a. Moving it to its final orbit

    b. Maneuvering in orbit

    c. Maintaining its attitude

    d. All of the above

2. The simplest example of a rocket is a (an) _____.

    a. brick

    b. airplane

    c. blimp

    d. balloon

3. At lift off, the Shuttle engines produce 26.6 billion watts of _____, equal to the output of 13 Hoover Dams.

    a. propellant

    b. power

    c. electricity

    d. heat

4. The higher the specific impulse the higher the rocket engine's _____.

    a. efficiency

    b. thrust

    c. mass

    d. reliability

5. In the ideal case, we'd like the pressure of the exhaust coming out of the nozzle to _____ the pressure of the atmosphere outside.

   a. disperse

   b. equal

   c. decrease

   d. minimize

6. In the simplest use of electrodynamic rockets, they need only some charged propellant and a (an) _____ _____.

   a. electric field

   b. ionic molecule

   c. high pressure

   d. high temperature

7. Under-expanded nozzles are the normal case for a rocket operating in a (an) _____, because the exit pressure is always _____ than the atmospheric pressure.

   a. ascent, higher

   b. atmosphere, lower

   c. shutdown, lower

   d. vacuum, higher

8. We keep a propellant's _____ _____ as low as possible to improve specific impulse for thermodynamic rockets.

   a. mass ratio

   b. total mass

   c. molecular mass

   d. tank volume

9. Which of the following is not an advantage of a cold-gas rocket engine?

   a. Extremely simple

   b. Low specific impulse

   c. Reliable

   d. Safe, low-temperature

10. When we have a large imbalance between positive and negative charges in a confined region, we have a (an) _____ _____.

    a. charged field

    b. electric field

    c. gravity field

    d. propulsion field

11. Electrodynamic rockets produce higher thrust by creating a higher

    _____ _____.

    a. charge density

    b. combustion pressure

    c. exhaust velocity

    d. ionic force

D. Matching:

Match the item in Column A with its description in Column B. You may use an item from Column B only once, but you won't use all of them.

Column A	*Column B*
1. Rocket ____	a. Force applied to an object over time
2. Thrust ____	b. Soup of ions and free electrons
3. Specific impulse ____	c. Repel each other
4. Impulse ____	d. Rocket ejects mass at high speed
5. Thermodynamic energy ____	e. Attract each other
6. Electrodynamic energy ____	f. Converts mass and energy into high-speed exhaust
7. Like charges ____	g. Rocket engine's "bang for the buck"
8. Plasma ____	h. Relate to energy available from charged particles
	i. Transfers to the propellant in the form of heat and pressure
	j. Force on a unit charge

E. True/False:

Place a **T** in the blank if the statement is true, and an **F** in the blank if it is false.

_____ 1. If we lower the mass flow rate (mdot) for a rocket engine, we increase its thrust.

_____ 2. The thrust a rocket produces depends only on the velocity of the propellant ejected and how much mass is ejected in a given time.

_____ 3. The velocity change delivered by a rocket engine depends on its efficiency and the ratio of its initial mass to its final mass.

_____ 4. Energized propellant converts to high-speed exhaust to create thrust.

_____ 5. When hot gases from a rocket engine pass the throat, they slow down in the nozzle to create more thrust.

_____ 6. Over-expanded nozzles typically occur at liftoff, decreasing the thrust.

_____ 7. Ions packed in a small space tend to repel each other, limiting the charge density and thus the thrust.

F. Short Answers (Things to Think About):

Write a short answer to each question.

1. What three things are rockets used for on launch vehicles and spacecraft?

2. Describe the inputs and outputs of the simplest version of a rocket system.

3. Define rocket thrust. Explain where it comes from in terms of Newton's Third Law of Motion.

4. Describe the relationship between rocket thrust, propellant mass flow rate and exhaust velocity.

5. Define specific impulse.

6. What are the two main categories of rockets in use? How are they classified?

7. What is charge? What is an ion?

8. What basic function does a nozzle serve for a thermodynamic rocket?

9. Describe the difference between over-expanded, under-expanded, and ideally expanded rocket nozzles. What is the exit pressure for an ideally expanded nozzle?

10. What two qualities of a thermodynamic rocket engine affect the specific impulse it can produce? How do we choose these qualities to produce the highest specific impulse?

11. Explain the basic operating principle of a cold-gas rocket. Give an example of their application.

12. Describe how we can use an electric field to accelerate ions.

13. Describe the relationship between charge density and thrust. Describe the relationship between electric-field strength and specific impulse.

14. Define plasma and give an everyday example. What is the main advantage of using plasma for electrodynamic propulsion?

G. List or Describe:

1. What limits how fast a rocket engine can eject mass? Consider the thermodynamic and the electrodynamic rockets.

Chapter 12 Rockets and Launch Vehicles

Section 12.2. Propulsion Systems

(Homework Problems: A1, A2, A4, A11, A30, A34, B4-B10)

A. Define, Describe, or Identify (Vocabulary):

1. Arcjet rocket

2. Bipropellant rockets

3. Check valves

4. Chemical rockets

5. Combustion chambers

6. Cryogenic

7. Electrostatic thruster

8. Exotic propulsion systems

9. Fuel

10. Hall-effect thruster (HET)

11. Hybrid propulsion systems

12. Hypergolic

13. Ion thruster

14. Monopropellant

15. Motor

16. Nuclear-thermal rocket

17. Oxidizer

18. Oxidizer/fuel ratio (O/F)

19. Plasma thrusters

20. Pressure-fed propellant system

21. Pressure-relief valves

22. Pressure sensors

23. Propellant management

24. Pulsed-plasma thrusters (PPT)

25. Pump-fed delivery system

26. Regulator

27. Resistojet

28. Solar sail

29. Solar-thermal rockets

30. Solid rocket

31. Storable propellants

32. Tau factor

33. Tethers

34. Thermoelectric rockets

35. Time dilation

B. Fill in the Blanks:

Fill in the blank with the word or words necessary to complete the statement.

1. Typical gas-storage pressures are _____ bar or higher.

2. Regardless of the propellant-delivery system, the pressure of propellants and pressurizing gases must be _____ at all times.

3. In a propellant delivery system, as high-pressure gas flows into a regulator, the gas pushes against a carefully designed _____.

4. _____ valves let liquid flow in only one direction.

5. In the Shuttle main engines, liquid _____ and liquid _____ combine in the most basic of chemical reactions.

6. Propellants that don't need a separate means of ignition are called _____.

7. The biggest advantage of monopropellant over bipropellant systems is _____.

8. A solid rocket motor's total burning area depends mostly on the inside _____ of the solid propellant.

9. An advantage of solar-thermal rocket engines is the abundant source of _____ _____.

10. A nuclear-thermal rocket uses its _____ to flow around the nuclear _____, absorbing _____ energy.

11. An electrodynamic rocket's high _____ _____ comes with a price tag—high _____ requirement and low _____.

12. Pulsed plasma thrusters have fairly low _____ _____ efficiency (20%), but they provide good _____ _____ with low _____.

13. A payload on the end of a long tether above the Shuttle is traveling _____ than orbital mechanics would require for its altitude.

14. In the twin paradox, if one sister leaves her twin and goes off on a space mission that travels near the _____ _____ _____, when she returns, she'll find her twin much _____ that she is.

C. Multiple Choice:

Circle the letter that correctly answers the question or completes the statement.

1. Which of the following is not a task of propellant management in a spacecraft's propulsion subsystem?
    a. Propellant storage
    b. Pressure control
    c. Tank insulation
    d. Temperature control

2. The main drawback to a pressure-fed propellant system is that very large quantities of propellant require very large quantities of the _____ _____.
    a. pressurizing gas
    b. valve controls
    c. feed lines
    d. electrical power

3. Pump-fed systems rely on pumps to take _____ pressure liquid and move it toward the combustion chamber at _____ pressure.
    a. high, low
    b. low, high
    c. zero, high
    d. high, medium

4. Which of the following is (are) thermodynamic rocket engine types?

    a. Chemical

    b. Solar thermal

    c. Thermoelectric

    d. All of the above

5. Combustion reactions must have a fuel plus an oxidizer, which combine, freeing a vast amount of _____ and forming the _____.

    a. exhaust, energy

    b. energy, momentum

    c. smoke, heat

    d. heat, exhaust

6. What is the main drawback to using cryogenic propellants for rocket propulsion?

    a. Low thrust

    b. Poor storability

    c. Low efficiency

    d. High boil off

7. A solid rocket motor's mass flow rate depends on its _____ rate and the _____ surface area.

    a. acceleration, smooth

    b. cure, total

    c. burn, burning

    d. mixing, rough

8. A well-designed hybrid rocket has the flexibility of a _____ system and the simplicity and density of a _____ motor.

    a. liquid, solid

    b. solid, liquid

    c. monopropellant, bipropellant

    d. hypergolic, cryogenic

9. Astronauts on the International Space Station rely on hydrazine resistojets to maintain the ISS's final mission _____ and _____.

    a. maneuver, position

    b. boost, temperature

    c. orbit, attitude

    d. rendezvous, vibration

10. The main limit on thermoelectric rocket thrust and efficiency is the amount of _____ available.

    a. power

    b. propellant

    c. velocity

    d. temperature

11. Which of the following is (are) electrodynamic rocket engines?

    a. Ion thruster

    b. Arcjet thruster

    c. Plasma thruster

    d. a and c above

12. _____ scientists pioneered many of the modern advances in Hall-effect thrusters.

    a. U.S.

    b. Russian

    c. European

    d. Japanese

13. When selecting a spacecraft's propulsion subsystem, which of the following must we consider before making a final decision?

    a. Mass performance

    b. Power requirements

    c. Technical risk

    d. All of the above

14. Light imparts a tiny _____ on any surface it strikes.

    a. shine

    b. vibration

    c. reflectance

    d. force

D. Matching:

Match the item in Column A with its description in Column B. You may use an item from Column B only once, but you won't use all of them.

Column A	*Column B*
1. Pressure regulator _____	a. One-time use
2. Hydrazine propellant _____	b. Needs no separate means of ignition
3. Pyrotechnic valve _____	c. Rocket grade hydrogen peroxide
4. Hypergolic rocket engines _____	d. A common composite solid fuel
5. Monopropellant _____	e. Once started are hard to stop
6. Aluminum _____	f. Could achieve a specific impulse of 800 seconds
7. Solid rocket motors _____	g. Uses Xenon—a safe, dense, inert gas
8. Solar-thermal rocket _____	h. Propels without ejecting mass
9. Ion thruster _____	i. May reduce pressure from 200 to 20 bar
10. Solar sail _____	j. Deploy below the Shuttle to deorbit
	k. Freezes at 0° Celsius
	l. Can burn rubber or plastic

E. True/False:

Place a **T** in the blank if the statement is true, and an **F** in the blank if it is false.

_____ 1. The Space Shuttle propellant pumps could empty an average-sized swimming pool in 1.5 seconds.

_____ 2. The ideal gas law tells us that a higher gas temperature causes a lower pressure.

_____ 3. Most spacecraft use storable hypergolic propellants for maneuvering.

_____ 4. The Shuttle's solid rocket motors have a specially made star-shaped core, so the thrust decreases 55 seconds into the flight to reduce acceleration and the effects of aerodynamic forces.

_____ 5. Similar to resistojets, arcjets can use almost any propellant.

_____ 6. Ion thrusters are an efficient propulsion option with very high thrust.

_____ 7. Even if we could develop efficient, onboard energy sources and rely on high specific impulse rockets, light speed would still limit travel.

F. Short Answers (Things to Think About):

Write a short answer to each question.

1. List the key elements of any propulsion subsystem. Describe how they relate to each other.

2. What are the four main tasks of propellant management for propulsion systems?

3. What are the main differences between pressure-fed and pump-fed propulsions systems? What are some of the advantages and disadvantages of each?

4. List the five basic types of thermodynamic rockets. Describe their basic operating principles.

5. Describe the functional difference between bipropellant and monopropellant liquid-chemical rockets. Compare their relative advantages and disadvantages.

6. What is the advantage of hypergolics over other propellants?

7. Describe the basic operating principle for solid-rocket motors. List some of their advantages and disadvantages. Give examples of their uses.

8. Explain how the shape of the propellant grain can affect the thrust profile for a solid-rocket motor. Give an example of how this shaping can help us gain an operational advantage.

9. Describe the basic operating principle of hybrid rockets. Compare their advantages and disadvantages to those for chemical bipropellant systems.

10. Describe the basic operating principle for solar-thermal rockets. Compare their advantages and disadvantages to those for chemical bipropellant systems.

11. List the two main types of thermoelectric rocket thrusters. Describe their basic operating principles. Compare their performances. Describe the basic design trade-offs engineers have among power, thrust, and specific impulse.

12. Explain the operating principle for nuclear-thermal rockets. Discuss the technical and political issues associated with their future uses.

13. What are the two main types of electrodynamic rockets in use? What is the primary difference between the two?

14. List the two main types of plasma thrusters. Describe their basic operating principles.

15. Discuss future uses of electrodynamic rockets on interplanetary, communication, and remote-sensing missions. What are advantages and disadvantages of these systems versus chemical-propulsion options?

16. List what we must consider when figuring out the total "cost" of a specific propulsion subsystem. Describe how the relative importance of these factors (text says "atoms", which is incorrect) would differ between an experimental-science mission by university students and a communication mission conducted by a commercial aerospace company.

17. What is the basic operating principle of a solar sail? Where does its thrust come from?

18. Describe how we could use a tether to de-orbit a spacecraft's upperstage. Why is the velocity change from a tether not completely "free"?

19. The starship Endeavor travels at 80% of the speed of light for one year (relative to the crew.) How much time will pass relative to people back on Earth?

20. What would be the best rocket technologies, or set of technologies, to use for a crewed Mars mission?

Chapter 12 Rockets and Launch Vehicles

Section 12.3. Launch Vehicles

(Homework Problems: A1-A5, C1-C5)

A. Define, Describe, or Identify (Vocabulary):

1. Dynamic pressure

2. g-load

3. Throttling

4. Thrust-to-weight ratio

5. Thrust-vector control (TVC)

B. Fill in the Blanks:

Fill in the blank with the word or words necessary to complete the statement.

1. A launch vehicle needs most of the same _____ as a spacecraft to deliver a payload from the ground into orbit.

2. Launch vehicle rockets often have the unique requirement to vary their thrust _____ for steering.

3. As with all control systems, a launch vehicle's NGC subsystem has _____ and _____.

4. A launch vehicle's _____ and _____ environments require all subsystems to be very rugged.

5. Because of their limited lifetimes, expendable launch vehicles typically rely on fairly simple _____ for main power during launch.

6. More than _____ of a typical launch vehicle's lift-off mass is propellant.

7. _____ consist of propellant tanks, rocket engines, and other supporting subsystems that are _____ to lighten the launch vehicle on the way to orbit.

8. By the time we add a fourth or fifth stage, the increased _____ and reduced _____ cancel out the small performance gain.

C. Multiple Choice:

Circle the letter that correctly answers the question or completes the statement.

1. Of the following challenges, which one sets a launch vehicle's propulsion subsystem apart from a spacecraft's?

    a. Thrust-to-weight ratio

    b. Throttling and thrust-vector control

    c. Nozzle design

    d. All of the above

2. Which of the following is <u>not</u> a propellant combination for launch vehicles with high thrust-to-weight ratios?

    a. Cryogenic

    b. Solid rockets

    c. Storable bipropellant

    d. Monopropellant

3. During launch, flight controllers continually monitor _____ from a launch vehicle's subsystems to ensure proper operations.

    a. time

    b. data

    c. telemetry

    d. radiation

4. Because most of a launch vehicle's volume contains _____ _____, their overall structural design is often based on them.

    a. wire bundles

    b. rocket engines

    c. propellant tanks

    d. payload systems

5. Which of the following is (are) launch vehicle mechanisms?

    a. Explosive bolts for staging

    b. Global Positioning System sensors

    c. Hydraulic arms

    d. a and c above

6. About _____ of a launch vehicle's mass is payload.

    a. 1%

    b. 5%

    c. 50%

    d. 80%

7. Staging increases a launch vehicle's _____ because of the extra sets of engines and their plumbing.

    a. acceleration

    b. reliability

    c. complexity

    d. dependability

D. Matching:

Match the item in Column A with its description in Column B. You may use an item from Column B only once, but you won't use all of them.

Column A	Column B
1. Throttling _____	a. Inflatable, thin-shelled tank
2. Astronaut g-load _____	b. Increases the total velocity for the same-sized vehicle
3. Thrust-vector control (TVC) _____	c. Decreases launch-vehicle costs
4. Aerospike engine nozzle _____	d. Near ideal expansion from launch to orbit
5. Original Atlas structure _____	e. No more than three during launch
6. Staging _____	f. Can direct engine to point thrust in desired direction
	g. Over-expanded exhaust
	h. Regulates flow of propellant in engine

E. True/False:

Place a **T** in the blank if the statement is true, and an **F** in the blank if it is false.

_____ 1. The Shuttle reduces the main engine's thrust from 104% to 65% during the peak dynamic pressure and the g-load phase of launch.

_____ 2. A nozzle's design altitude for ideal expansion is about three-fourths of the way from the altitude of engine ignition to the altitude of engine cutoff.

_____ 3. Navigation, guidance, and control sensors typically include accelerometers and gyroscopes.

_____ 4. Range Safety Officers are ready to send a self-destruct command if a launch vehicle strays beyond the planned flight path and endangers people or property.

_____ 5. Launch-vehicle staging decreases the total payload delivered to space for the same-sized vehicle.

F. Short Answers (Things to Think About):

Write a short answer to each question.

1. What are the two biggest differences affecting the design of launch vehicles versus spacecraft?

2. What unique challenges are presented by a launch vehicle's propulsion subsystem versus a spacecraft's propulsion subsystem?

3. Give examples for why a launch vehicle may need to throttle its rocket engines.

4. Describe the differences and similarities between launch vehicles and spacecraft in these subsystems: navigation, guidance, and control; communication and data handling; electrical power; and structure and mechanisms.

5. What are the advantages and disadvantages of staging?

6. Given the state-of-the-art in rocket technology, what other options for launch-vehicle design could offer lower cost access to space?

UNIT 4: Mission Operations and Management

Chapter 13 Space Operations

13.1. Mission Operations Systems

(Homework Problems: A3-A13, A25-A27, B3-B7)

A. Define, Describe, or Identify (Vocabulary):

1. Azimuth

2. Clean room

3. Commands

4. Communication

5. Communication architecture

6. Control center

7. Crosslink

8. Data rate

9. Downlink

10. Environmental testing

11. Forward link

12. Functional testing

13. Ground stations

14. Omni-directional

15. Power-flux density

16. Range

17. Real time

18. Real-time commands

19. Receiver

20. Relay satellites

21. Return link

22. Signal strength

23. Spacecraft

24. Stored commands

25. Telemetry

26. Transmitter

27. Uplink

B. Fill in the Blanks:

Fill in the blank with the word or words necessary to complete the statement.

1. Today's space missions build on more than 40 years of space _____.

2. Computer-driven tools let technicians turn electronic _____ directly into finished _____.

3. After thermal/vacuum testing, we must repeat the _____ tests to find out if anything broke. If something did, then we must fix it and _____ it again.

4. During testing, a _____ _____ subjects a spacecraft structure to the dynamic loading environment it will experience during launch.

5. As a guest passenger (_____ payload), a spacecraft can't do anything that may put the main mission at _____.

6. At launch ranges, because of range safety concerns, not all physically possible inclinations are allowed _____.

7. Worldwide _____ _____ help the mission operators know where their satellite is at all times.

8. To communicate well from one spacecraft to another or to a ground station, we must have a transmitter and a receiver that must be using the same language or _____.

9. Spacecraft often rely on _____ antennas that point toward the receiver at the ground station to make more _____ use of their transmitter's power.

10. NASA's Spaceflight Tracking and Data Network includes ground-based antennas at _____, New Mexico and the space-based portion using the Tracking and Data Relay Satellites in _____ orbits.

11. The U.S. Air Force's Space Surveillance Network tracks objects in low-Earth orbit as small as _____ centimeters long.

12. The U.S. Air Force Satellite Control Network connects with control centers at _____ Air Force Base, Colorado, and _____ Air Force Base, California.

C. Multiple Choice:

Circle the letter that correctly answers the question or completes the statement.

1. Without mission operations systems, space missions couldn't generate the _____ the designers had in mind.

   a. orbits

   b. products

   c. thrust

   d. power

2. Which of the following is (are) a basic phase of a spacecraft's life?

   a. Manufacturing

   b. Launch

   c. Operations

   d. All of the above

3. To ensure the highest quality, most spacecraft parts are assembled and integrated in dedicated _____ _____.

    a. manufacturing plants

    b. clean rooms

    c. supply companies

    d. user centers

4. Which of the following is <u>not</u> a function performed by ground support equipment?

    a. Lifting with huge cranes

    b. Communications

    c. Transportation from the manufacturing plant

    d. Electrical power

5. The solar simulation chamber simulates the _____ _____ input to test solar cell output and thermal control-system design.

    a. solar flare

    b. solar radiation

    c. solar corona

    d. a and c above

6. Hitchhiker payloads depend on the primary payload to set _____ for launch and launch-vehicle _____.

    a. requirements, interfaces

    b. time, size

    c. location, time

    d. delays, pad

7. Which of the following is (are) examples of telemetry data from a satellite?

    a. Rocket engine temperature

    b. Tank pressure

    c. Battery voltage

    d. All of the above

8. After receiving a command through an uplink, a spacecraft's communication subsystem _____ it back to the operators through the _____.

    a. drops, droplink

    b. reverses, commlink

    c. echoes, downlink

    d. returns, crosslink

9. Which of the following is <u>not</u> a condition to consider when humans communicate?

    a. Direction

    b. Distance

    c. Language

    d. Speed

10. If we put a parabola-shaped mirror on one side of a bright light bulb, we effectively _____ most of the light energy into a smaller area.

    a. scatter

    b. concentrate

    c. decrease

    d. accelerate

11. What types of activities do space operators do?

    a. Monitor subsystem performance

    b. Collect and distribute mission data

    c. Evaluate users need for data

    d. a and b above

D. Matching:

Match the item in Column A with its description in Column B. You may use an item from Column B only once, but you won't use all of them.

Column A

1. Spacecraft manufacturing ____

2. Clean room ____

3. Acoustic chamber ____

4. Vandenberg range ____

5. Internet ____

6. Watch-dog timer ____

7. Deep Space Network ____

Column B

a. Tracks time since the last communication

b. An antenna in Spain, Australia, and California

c. Improves power density

d. Shakes a spacecraft at specific frequencies

e. Systems that support design, assembly, integration, and testing

f. Carefully controlled work environment

g. Subjects spacecraft to high noise loads

h. Complex communication system and a valuable link for distributing mission data

i. All launches go toward the south

E. True/False:

Place a **T** in the blank if the statement is true, and an **F** in the blank if it is false.

_____ 1. For the first space missions, operators had to invent nearly everything to make a mission possible.

_____ 2. Smart mission managers look for hardware or software tools that they can re-use throughout a mission's lifetime or for later missions.

_____ 3. Anechoic chambers test onboard communications software for correct signal strengths.

_____ 4. Because the Sea Launch platform is mobile, mission planners can place their booster and payload right on the North Pole to gain the maximum benefit from Earth's eastward rotation.

_____ 5. Only when a launch vehicle gets above the horizon can it make contact with the mission control center.

_____ 6. Car radios receive signals from radio stations in the form of electromagnetic radiation.

_____ 7. A light bulb's brightness decreases as we move farther away from it.

F. Short Answer (Things to Think About):

Write a short answer to each question.

1. Describe what goes into the mission operations systems.

2. What's the purpose of a clean room during spacecraft manufacturing? What does it mean to have a Class 10,000 clean room? Is that cleaner than a Class 1,000 clean room?

3. List and describe four types of test facilities used for spacecraft integration and tests.

4. What four pieces make up a launch complex that prepares and boosts a payload into orbit?

5. For a space mission, what communications must take place? Describe the four pieces of Space Communication Architecture.

6. For space missions, what are real-time operations? If real-time communication isn't possible, what are the other types of operations?

7. What is a spacecraft "safe" mode and how can it save a mission?

8. What four conditions must be compatible for two people or two spacecraft to communicate? What does it mean to have a signal-to-noise ratio greater than 1.0?

9. Describe the steps a radio signal must take to get from a radio station to your car speaker in a form you can enjoy.

10. Why would it be a bad idea to use the U.S. Air Force's Satellite Control Network to uplink commands to our FireSat satellite? Could we ask the Space Surveillance Network to track our 0.3 meter x 0.3 meter x 0.3 meter spacecraft?

Chapter 13 Space Operations

13.2. Mission Management and Operations

(Homework Problems: A1-A5, B7-B10, C4-C6)

A. Define, Describe, or Identify (Vocabulary):

1. Commissioning

2. Critical path

3. Design-for-manufacture

4. Earned value

5. Flight controllers

6. Flight rules

7. Ground-systems specialist

8. Launch-readiness review

9. Mission autonomy

10. Mission timeline

11. Operators

12. Payload specialists

13. Simulations

14. Slack

15. Subsystem specialists

16. Team norms

17. Work breakdown structure (WBS)

B. Fill in the Blanks:

Fill in the blank with the word or words necessary to complete the statement.

1. Behind all the expensive space hardware are _____
    _____.

2. One of the biggest challenges for a mission manager is to _____
    the space systems engineering process.

3. Mission managers must juggle the individual demands of mission _____ and those who carry out the mission.

4. The most precious mission resource is the _____.

5. Other teams must apply the same systems-engineering process to create critical _____-_____ systems.

6. The launch team's job starts _____ _____ the spacecraft arrives at the pad.

7. At the launch site, the launch team's main focus is on two major tasks: _____ _____ and _____ _____.

8. When everything and everybody is in place, the launch vehicle and spacecraft are happy and healthy, and the weather is cooperating, launch controllers take part in the final _____-_____ _____.

9. For space communication missions, operators may need to oversee _____ _____ and the _____ _____ passing through the spacecraft.

10. Project team leaders can solve or avoid team problems by working on areas such as _____ set for the team, how well the team _____ together, and the method to resolve _____.

11. The Work Breakdown Structure for large projects, such as Milstar, fills _____ of documentation.

12. One of the benefits of network scheduling is to show us which _____ we can do at the same time.

C. Multiple Choice:

Circle the letter that correctly answers the question or completes the statement.

1. Which of the following are space mission tasks for ordinary people?

    a. Ordering parts

    b. Assembling components

    c. Tracking budgets

    d. All of the above

2. Which of the following is <u>not</u> a mission manager's task?

    a. Define mission objectives

    b. Trade mission and system requirements

    c. Establish operations systems

    d. Determine the mission need

3. During system assembly, integration, and test, workers must _____ components for form, fit, and function.

    a. screen

    b. eliminate

    c. design

    d. build

4. From the first concept through flight readiness, one of the focuses for a Manufacturing Team is _____ _____.

    a. system AIT

    b. systems engineering

    c. computer drawings

    d. correct machinery

5. For complex missions, operators working with dedicated engineering teams must define _____ and _____ requirements to conduct simulations and plan coordinated training programs.

    a. tests, plans

    b. costs, schedule

    c. hardware, software

    d. people, programs

6. Assembly, integration, and testing is a coordinated effort by which of the following?

    a. Assembly technicians

    b. System integrators

    c. Testers

    d. All of the above

7. At launch time, the _____-_____ team for launch monitors the launch vehicle and spacecraft systems.

    a. flight-control

    b. launch-control

    c. readiness-review

    d. a or b above

8. Mission data processing and handling is one of four key responsibilities for the _____ team.

    a. design

    b. manufacturing

    c. launch

    d. operations

9. After a spacecraft goes through commissioning and is ready to start performing its mission, the operations team moves into the _____ _____.

    a. post launch

    b. normal operations

    c. everyday planning

    d. data flow

10. In addition to their training, commanding, and data-handling duties, the operations team must maintain the operations systems that support them by making which of the following?

    a. Remote-tracking site repairs

    b. Control-center hardware upgrades

    c. Relay satellite link connections

    d. All of the above

11. Smart project managers have useful tools in their kit to help them keep things on _____ and within _____.

    a. schedule, budget

    b. time, limits

    c. target, bounds

    d. track, reason

12. A forward pass through a network diagram finds the _____ - _____ time and the _____ - _____ for each activity by moving from the left to right on a project diagram.

    a. earliest-start, earliest-finish

    b. latest-start, earliest-finish

    c. earliest-start, latest-finish

    d. latest-start, latest-finish

D. Matching:

Match the item in Column A with its description in Column B. You may use an item from Column B only once, but you won't use all of them.

Column A	*Column B*
1. Minimum resources ____	a. Charge batteries and fill propellant tanks
2. Launch vehicle servicing ____	b. Poised to destroy an errant launch vehicle
3. Launch-support people ____	c. Run tracking stations and watch weather
4. Range Safety Officer ____	d. Setting goals and increasing interaction
5. Flight Dynamics Officer ____	e. Conflict resolution method
6. Team working together ____	f. One-third of a large program's cost
7. Network diagrams ____	g. Labor, money, and time
8. Operations costs ____	h. Monitors Shuttle's launch trajectory
	i. Human errors cause mission losses
	j. Roadmap of the activities that come before and after

E. True/False:

Place a **T** in the blank if the statement is true, and an **F** in the blank if it is false.

_____ 1. Other tasks, such as mission management, span the life of the mission.

_____ 2. A mission timeline would lay out when in the countdown sequence to cut off external power.

_____ 3. Upper-level winds don't affect a launch vehicle, so flight directors don't monitor them.

_____ 4. After launch, the launch recovery team takes over a space mission.

_____ 5. When its time for launch the operations team needs to be closely familiar with every aspect of the mission and what to do when something goes wrong.

_____ 6. Project team leaders are responsible for their team members knowing the relationships among the organizational tasks.

_____ 7. One powerful aspect of the Critical Path Method is the ability to accurately control a project by shifting resources.

_____ 8. Commercial space missions prefer less autonomy onboard their spacecraft to minimize engineering costs.

F. Short Answers (Things to Think About):

Write a short answer to each question.

1. What eight things must mission managers do to create a completely designed, assembled, and tested space system?

2. List eight operations tasks that operators must do during the life of a space mission.

3. Describe a mission timeline and how managers use it to script a space mission.

4. What tests lead to the launch-readiness review? What happens at this review?

5. Describe the roles of the launch director and range-safety officer in getting a launch vehicle and its spacecraft safely into orbit.

6. What positions make up an operations team? Which one takes charge of the team for the Space Shuttle?

7. Describe the job of operations-team leaders. What tools can help them in their management tasks?

8. List three benefits to network scheduling methods, such as the Program Evaluation and Review Technique and the Critical-path Method.

9. What five characteristics of effective program control help the program manager gain confidence with owners and users that a successful mission is underway?

10. For the FireSat Network Diagram (Figure 13-33), why did we need the earliest-start and earliest-finish times? How and why did we compute the latest-start and latest-finish times?

11. How does spacecraft autonomy save mission costs? Why aren't all spacecraft able to function completely on their own?

G. List or Describe

1. Do you agree that more highly complex space missions start successfully now than they did 20 years ago? Why or why not?

Chapter 14 Using Space

Section 14.1. The Space Industry

(Homework Problems: A1, A2, A5, A7, D1-D5)

A. Define, Describe, or Identify (Vocabulary):

1. Capital market acceptance

2. Commercialization

3. Deregulation

4. Geographic Information System (GIS)

5. Global Positioning System (GPS)

6. Global space industry

7. Globalization

B. Fill in the Blanks:

Fill in the blank with the word or words necessary to complete the statement.

1. Recent surveys show that the average person in the U.S. uses space assets about _____ times per day.

2. As of 2000, more than _____ functional spacecraft were orbiting Earth.

3. Today, space is truly a _____ activity.

4. Twenty years ago space use was mainly a _____ activity, but today, the trend is more toward _____ or _____ ventures.

5. Space-related business opportunities come from _____ many traditional government-run activities.

6. Companies use _____ _____ (government) data to provide useful products and services worldwide.

7. Private companies have taken the lead in linking data sources to data users by turning _____ _____ into productive information.

8. The built in "_____ _____" advantages of space-based equipment continue to be a good means for delivering services and gathering information across nations, regions, and the entire globe.

C. Multiple Choice:

Circle the letter that correctly answers the question or completes the statement.

1. In 1969, the former _____ _____ and the U.S. were in a struggle to see who would be first in space.

    a. Great Britain

    b. French Republic

    c. Soviet Union

    d. Chinese nation

2. According to industry projections, most new spacecraft in coming years will be in _____.

    a. remote sensing

    b. interplanetary

    c. science

    d. telecommunications

3. More than 20 countries have active national space programs, with the U.S., Russia, _____, _____, and _____ leading the way.

    a. Europe, China, Japan

    b. Israel, India, Brazil

    c. Australia, Argentina, Chile

    d. Egypt, Venezuela, Greece

4. Almost any country can start its own space program because fairly low-cost _____ opportunities are available.

    a. financing

    b. launch

    c. travel

    d. engineering

5. In 1996, _____% of the global government spending on space came from the U.S. (civil and military).

    a. 25

    b. 50

    c. 70

    d. 90

6. Which of the following is (are) space-related services?

    a. Telecommunications

    b. Navigation

    c. Remote sensing

    d. All of the above

7. _____ communities around the world are more aware of the huge growth potential of space-related products and services.

    a. Transportation

    b. Recreation

    c. Financial

    d. Ethnic

8. Farmers use _____ _____ _____
   tools to analyze and manage their crops.

   a. Geographic Information System

   b. the latest computerized

   c. modern farming technology

   d. collective farming technical

D. Matching:

Match the item in Column A with its description in Column B. You may use an item from Column B only once, but you won't use all of them.

Column A	Column B
1. Microelectronics ____	a. Used by automobile manufacturers for stereos and sport trim
2. Personal telecommunication systems ____	b. Small-to-medium companies tend to innovate
3. Global Positioning System ____	c. Uses remote sensing images to estimate population growth-patterns
4. McDonalds© ____	d. Launch vehicle made by Orbital Sciences Corp.
5. Iridium Co. ____	e. Makes designing and building spacecraft cheaper
6. Pegasus ____	f. New space service in the U.S. and Europe
	g. Declared bankruptcy after deploying 66 satellites
	h. Uses GIS information to monitor forests

E. True/False:

Place a **T** in the blank if the statement is true, and an **F** in the blank if it is false.

_____ 1. In addition to hand built systems, satellite constellations exist that used mass produced spacecraft and off the shelf hardware.

_____ 2. Mission operations for the Space Shuttle won't ever transition to commercial enterprises.

_____ 3. Shipping companies use GPS to track inventory, thus streamlining their tracking systems.

_____ 4. Insurance companies use geographic information systems to assess claims following a flood or fire disaster.

_____ 5. Mergers and acquisitions among space industry giants reduce the number of companies competing for space contracts.

F. Short Answers (Things to Think About):

Write a short answer to each question.

1. List and describe emerging trends in the space industry.

2. List the four main market areas for commercial space activities. Give examples of each.

3. What are the three most important areas for space-related services? Give examples of each.

4. Describe what we mean by a value-added service.

5. Give examples of how we might use space capabilities to take advantage of the deregulation of electrical power utilities in the world.

Chapter 14 Using Space

14.2. Space Politics

(Homework Problems: A2-A5, B2-B5, C4-C7)

A. Define, Describe, or Identify (Vocabulary):

1. Department of Transportation (DOT)

2. Federal Communications Commission (FCC)

3. International Telecommunications Union (ITU)

4. National and regional security

5. National image

B. Fill in the Blanks:

Fill in the blank with the word or words necessary to complete the statement.

1. Until the early 1960s, the main motivation for space missions was
   _____.

2. Space systems have become a force _____, allowing the modern
   military to do more with less.

3. Showing technical excellence in the U.S. space program advertises its national
   competence in military _____ and _____.

4. Nations pursue space activities to boost the competitive advantage of their own
   national _____.

5. Enhancing national _____ can conflict directly with supporting
   national _____.

6. Governments develop rules of international _____ that shape the context in which all space missions must operate.

7. Space is not a _____ arena, meaning everyone should carry out activities in space according to international law.

8. Each nation must police its own people and industries to make sure they _____ with international law in space.

9. The Federal _____ _____ manages radio frequency assignments for operations over the U.S. territory.

10. The U.S. _____ Department must approve exports of all space technology.

C. Multiple Choice:

Circle the letter that correctly answers the question or completes the statement.

1. Which of the following is <u>not</u> a reason for governments to pursue space activities?

   a. Promote national image

   b. Collect government taxes

   c. Enhance national and regional security

   d. Advance science and technology

2. Which of the following is (are) national security space systems?

   a. Spy (remote sensing)

   b. Early warning

   c. Communication

   d. All of the above

3. Funding for advanced space technologies goes to _____, national _____, and commercial _____.

   a. states, museums, galleries

   b. universities, laboratories, industries

   c. cities, parks, enterprises

   d. colleges, departments, institutions

4. National industries need to create marketable space-related products and services such as _____.

    a. data products

    b. spacecraft

    c. launch vehicles

    d. all of the above

5. The competitive edge in making space products comes from _____.

    a. modern and efficient ways to produce many spacecraft

    b. operating space systems economically

    c. cutting corners on reliability

    d. a and b above

6. The seven principles of space law come from five space _____ to which various countries subscribe.

    a. judgments

    b. lawsuits

    c. treaties

    d. rulings

7. International law says that no one can put _____ weapons in space.

    a. nuclear

    b. explosive

    c. dangerous

    d. offensive

8. International law states that if you launched it, you must keep _____ of it.

    a. control

    b. track

    c. ownership

    d. inspection

9. The International Telecommunications Union (ITU) provides equal access to orbital _____ and radio _____ .

    a. information, stations

    b. altitudes, licenses

    c. positions, frequencies

    d. arrangements, music

D. Matching:

Match the item in Column A with its description in Column B. You may use an item from Column B only once, but you won't use all of them.

Column A

1. Space race _____

2. Military space spending _____

3. "Buy American" _____

4. Registered spacecraft _____

5. International Telecommunications Union _____

6. Kodiak Island launch site _____

Column B

a. United Nations tracks who owns what

b. New facility approved by the U.S. Department of Transportation

c. International laws regulate this

d. Increased since the end of the Cold War

e. Demonstrating superiority of political system

f. International law uses typical practices

g. Frowns on selling geostationary slots

h. Purchase products and services from U.S. companies

E. True/False:

Place a **T** in the blank if the statement is true, and an **F** in the blank if it is false.

_____ 1. Space programs can also be useful for cementing relationships among friendly nations to further foreign-policy objectives.

_____ 2. Funding space activities at universities attracts students into technical fields and increases the pool of qualified space specialists.

_____ 3. When governments subsidize the space industry, it usually hurts their economies, which creates negative feedback, making it harder to fund space activities.

_____ 4. People have a right to use outer space only after they own the part they want to use.

_____ 5. The U.S. Department of Transportation works with NASA, DoD, the FAA, and other agencies to regulate launch vehicles and launch sites.

F. Short Answers (Things to Think About):

Write a short answer to each question.

1. According to industry expert Jim Oberg, what are the four main reasons nations pursue space activities? Give historic examples of each.

2. List and discuss the seven key principles that fashion international space activities.

3. Compare and contrast the Federal Communications Commission in the U.S. and the International Telecommunications Union.

G. List or Describe:

1. Do you think countries that colonize the Moon or Mars should be allowed to own the property they colonize? Why or why not?

Chapter 14 Using Space

Section 14.3. Space Economics

(Homework Problems: A1, A2, A5-A8, C1-C4)

A. Define, Describe, or Identify (Vocabulary):

1. Cost-estimating relationships (CERs)

2. Engineering models

3. Flight model

4. Flight spare

5. Internal rate of return

6. Life-cycle cost

7. Life cycle

8. Reliability

9. Space qualification

10. Test models

B. Fill in the Blanks:

Fill in the blank with the word or words necessary to complete the statement.

1. No matter how advanced the technology, or committed the political will, if the organization can't afford a space mission, it won't _____ _____ the ground.

2. The Clementine mission to the Moon was an example of a _____- _____ mission.

3. Enthusiasm for reliable space components can lead to over- _____ and higher system _____.

4. Going from 80% to 90% reliability costs much _____ than going from 50% to 60%.

5. Besides the launch vehicle's costs, we must consider all the related costs of operations systems to _____ the spacecraft and launch vehicle, _____ the launch site, and monitor _____ before, during, and after launch.

6. Part of the cost for mission operations is related to the _____ needed to connect the operators with their spacecraft and give them the tools to do their jobs.

7. A large part of operations costs relate to the _____ of people required.

8. The insurance for a _____ spacecraft launching on a _____ launch vehicle could be far more expensive than for a _____ design on a _____ launch vehicle.

9. Mission sponsors use _____ _____ Relationships as planning tools before committing a lot of money to a project.

10. Often, government-funded space missions try to get as much _____ or other information as possible for the money spent.

11. A commercial space mission's design and development depends largely on the company's _____ _____.

C. Multiple Choice:

Circle the letter that correctly answers the question or completes the statement.

1. Life-cycle cost of a space mission includes the cost of design, manufacture, launch, and _____.

    a. operations

    b. testing

    c. reuse

    d. transport

2. A traditional satellite is electronically equal to about _____ color TV sets.

    a. 2

    b. 10

    c. 80

    d. 200

3. If we want a strap to deploy a spacecraft's panel on orbit, we could attach _____ explosive bolts to ensure it releases.

    a. 1

    b. 2

    c. many

    d. larger

4. To cut costs and increase performance, commercial missions choose _____ off-the-shelf computers and other components.

    a. designer

    b. space

    c. commercial

    d. rejected

5. In general, cost and reliability have a (an) _____ relationship.

    a. inverse

    b. exponential

    c. impossible

    d. unpredictable

6. Which of the following is <u>not</u> a spacecraft model type that we need to build to get one working model in space?

    a. Engineering

    b. Test

    c. Flight

    d. Practice

7. During manufacturing and testing procedures, not only are the test articles _____ and the procedures _____-intensive, but also we must factor in the cost of the _____.

    a. inexpensive, time, workforce

    b. large, cost, time

    c. complicated, manpower, propellant

    d. expensive, labor, facilities

8. The more a spacecraft can do for itself, the more it can operate on its own, so it needs a (an) _____ expensive operations framework on the ground.

    a. more

    b. highly

    c. less

    d. overly

9. Insurance companies charge a premium of _____% to _____% of the total costs for a satellite and launch.

    a. 1, 2

    b. 5, 10

    c. 15, 30

    d. 50, 60

10. Commercial space-related businesses usually provide a product or service with the goal of making a _____ for their investors.

    a. profit

    b. living

    c. return

    d. success

D. Matching:

Match the item in Column A with its description in Column B. You may use an item from Column B only once, but you won't use all of them.

Column A	Column B
1. PoSat-1 costs ____	a. Use high-quality, duplicate or triplicate components
2. Component reliability ____	b. Cut the end-to-end test with bad consequences
3. UoSat 2 design ____	c. Operations costs are significant
4. Hubble tests ____	d. Third leg of a space mission triad
5. Launch costs ____	e. Challenger replacement cost came from the national budget
6. Cost of Endeavour ____	f. Life-cycle costs were a mere $2.1 million
	g. Uses commercial off-the-shelf computers
	h. Vary from $5000 to $30,000 per kilogram

E. True/False:

Place a **T** in the blank if the statement is true, and an **F** in the blank if it is false.

_____ 1. A space-qualified component typically must meet high military or NASA standards, so it may cost ten times more than a commercial version.

_____ 2. Sometimes we can restore and use a spacecraft's engineering or test models as a flight spare.

_____ 3. Government space missions are self-insured, so tax dollars go to replace a failed spacecraft.

_____ 4. Commercial space companies buy space insurance to protect themselves from known mission risks.

_____ 5. Space missions cost slightly less than gold per kilogram.

F. Short Answers (Things to Think About):

Write a short answer to each question.

1. Define the life-cycle cost of a space mission. What four mission activities make up the life-cycle cost?

2. Explain why space-qualified hardware is more expensive than hardware tested on Earth.

3. Define reliability. What is the relationship between reliability and cost?

4. Describe the difference between an engineering model, test model, flight model, and flight spare.

5. Describe your thought process in deciding to invest in a fairly risky space venture. What risks would you take and what return on investment would be appropriate?

6. Discuss the concept of space mission insurance. For what types of missions would it be most appropriate? Least appropriate?

7. Describe the effects on return on investment of a launch failure, and subsequent mission delay, on a business venture in space.

8. Describe two key differences between government and commercially sponsored space missions.

9. Study some of the everyday machines you encounter (automobile, photocopier, toaster, washing machine, and so on). How would the design and manufacture be different if no one could service the machine after it was built?

10. How would the planning and execution of a space project change as you vary the internal rate of return required by investors?

Chapter 15 Manned Space Explorations

Section 15.1. U.S. Manned Space Program

(Homework Problems: A1-A3, B3-B6)

A. Define, Describe, or Identify (Vocabulary):

1. Project Apollo

2. Project Gemini

3. Project Mercury

B. Fill in the Blanks:

Fill in the blank with the word or words necessary to complete the statement.

1. America's first manned space flight program was called _____
   _____.

2. _____ _____ became the first American to orbit
   Earth.

3. In 1961, President _____ _____ _____
   committed America to putting an astronaut on the Moon before the end of the
   decade.

4. Several of the early _____ flights traveled to the
   _____, orbited it, and returned to Earth.

5. On July 20, 1969, _____ _____ was the first man
   to walk on the Moon.

6. The U.S. space program was stopped for almost two years when astronauts
   _____ _____, _____
   _____, and _____ _____ were killed
   in a launch-pad fire.

C. Multiple Choice:

Circle the letter that correctly answers the question or completes the statement.

1. Which of the following was <u>not</u> a U.S. space program in the 1960s and 1970s?

    a. Project Shuttle

    b. Project Mercury

    c. Project Gemini

    d. Project Skylab

2. Which of the following was (were) chosen as the original U.S. astronauts?

    a. Scott Carpenter

    b. Gordon Cooper

    c. John Glenn

    d. All of the above

3. The first manned launch of Project Mercury was _____ and lasted for only _____ minutes.

    a. orbital, 90

    b. suborbital, 15

    c. disappointing, 5

    d. dangerous, 3

4. The original goal of Project Mercury was to put someone into orbit for _____ _____.

    a. weightless experiments

    b. endurance records

    c. one day

    d. engineering challenges

5. Which of the following was not an objective in Project Gemini?

    a. Improve methods needed for a lunar mission

    b. Put two people in space

    c. Achieve the first walk in space

    d. Drink Tang™ from a cup in space

6. Apollo _____ had to be aborted due to an explosion in the spacecraft.

    a. 1

    b. 11

    c. 13

    d. 17

7. To eliminate the fire threat that had killed three astronauts, NASA modified the _____ _____ and the astronaut's _____ _____.

    a. launch schedule, breathing rate

    b. command module, space suits

    c. booster rocket, life insurance

    d. propellant type, equipment list

D. Matching:

Match the item in Column A with its description in Column B. You may use an item from Column B only once, but you won't use all of them.

Column A	Column B
1. U.S. first satellite _____	a. Second man on the Moon
2. Project Mercury _____	b. Orbited Earth three times
3. John Glenn _____	c. Six manned landings on the Moon
4. Project Gemini _____	d. First two-person capsule
5. Buzz Aldrin _____	e. Suborbital flights only
6. Project Apollo _____	f. Conducted 19 unmanned test flights
	g. Launched in 1958
	h. Orbited Earth only one time

E. True/False:

Place a **T** in the blank if the statement is true, and an **F** in the blank if it is false.

_____ 1. The U.S. space program from 1961 to 1975 included the Apollo-Soyuz joint mission with the Soviets.

_____ 2. Project Mercury's mission was to find out if a human could survive space travel and how space travel might affect the human body.

_____ 3. One of Project Gemini's objectives was to rendezvous and dock with a Soviet space station.

_____ 4. The Project Gemini flights convinced scientists that space flight was too dangerous to continue.

_____ 5. Many people have called the Apollo 11 landing on the Moon the greatest scientific and engineering accomplishment in history.

F. Short Answers (Things to Think About):

Write a short answer to each question.

1. Who was the first American in space?

2. Which American space program landed a human on the Moon?

3. Who was the first person to walk on the Moon?

4. Which U.S. space flight carried the first crew? Which U.S. space flight was the first to place two people in space?

5. Who was the first American to orbit the Earth?

Chapter 15 Manned Space Explorations

ction 15.2. Soviet Manned Space Program

(Homework Problems: A1-A3, B3-B6, C1-C7, E2-4)

Define, Describe, or Identify (Vocabulary):

1. Soyuz

2. Voskhod

3. Vostok

Fill in the Blanks:

ll in the blank with the word or words necessary to complete the statement.

1. Russia's first manned space flight program was called _____.

2. _____ _____ became the first man to escape from Earth's atmosphere into space.

3. In 1963, _____ _____ was the first woman in space.

4. The last two _____ satellites were in preparation for Russia's first manned space flight.

5. On March 18, 1965, _____ _____ was the first man to "walk in space".

6. The Soviet space program was stopped for over one year when _____ _____ died after Soyuz 1 crashed.

Multiple Choice:

rcle the letter that correctly answers the question or completes the statement.

1. Which of the following was (were) <u>not</u> a Soviet space flight program in the 1960s to 1980s?

    a. Salyut

    b. Vostok

    c. Soyuz

    d. Voskhod

2. Which of the following was chosen as the first woman in space?

    a. Olga Korbut

    b. Anna Pavlova

    c. Svetlana Savitskaya

    d. Valentina Tereshkova

3. The first satellite launched into space was _____.

    a. Laika

    b. Sputnik

    c. Muttnik

    d. Vostok

4. What initial advantage did the Soviets have to put the first man in space?

    a. Weightless experiments

    b. Endurance records

    c. Large rockets

    d. Willing volunteers

5. Which of the following was <u>not</u> an objective in Soyuz?

    a. Docking

    b. Preparing for their first space stations

    c. Transferring crew members in space

    d. Putting a chimpanzee in space

6. Soyuz _____ and _____ fulfilled the mission of docking and transferring crew members in space.

    a. 1, 2

    b. 3, 4

    c. 4, 5

    d. 7, 9

7. Which of the following was <u>not</u> a goal of the Soviet space flight program?

    a. Designing cool space suits

    b. Launching Troika, a three person capsule

    c. Sending an American to the Moon

    d. All of the above

Matching:

atch the item in Column A with its description in Column B. You may use an item from Column only once, but you won't use all of them.

Column A	Column B
Soviet's first satellite ____	a. Three person capsule
Alexei Leonov ____	b. First to escape from Earth's atmosphere into space
Yuri Gagarin ____	c. Spent three days in orbit
Soyuz ____	d. Means "union"
Voskhod ____	e. First dog in space
Valentina Tereshkova ____	f. First person to "walk in space"
	g. Sputnik
	h. Famous Russian ballet dancer

True/False:

ace a **T** in the blank if the statement is true, and an **F** in the blank if it is false.

_____ 1. Major Yuri Gagarin was the first man in space.

_____ 2. The Soviet space walk happened about two months before the Americans walked in space.

_____ 3. The Soviet space flight programs were way ahead of the U.S. space programs.

_____ 4. The Soviets resumed their flights immediately after Cosmonaut Vladimir Komarov died when Soyuz 1 crashed.

_____ 5. Soyuz consisted of three modules: an instrument module with rocket engines, an orbital module, and a descent module.

F. Short Answers (Things to Think About):

Write a short answer to each question.

1. What is the name of the first spacecraft successfully launched by the Soviet Union?

2. What is the name of the first man in space?

3. Who was the first Russian to walk in space?

4. What was the Soyuz series of manned spacecraft designed to do?

Chapter 15 Manned Space Explorations

Section 15.3. Case Study: The Space Shuttle

(Homework Problems: A1-A6, C1-C5)

A. Define, Describe, or Identify (Vocabulary):

1. Electrical power system (EPS)

2. Environmental control and life support system (ECLSS)

3. External tank (ET)

4. Fuel cell

5. Orbital maneuvering system (OMS)

6. Orbiter

7. Shuttle Mission Simulators (SMSs)

8. Solid rocket booster (SRB)

9. Space Shuttle Main Engines (SSMEs)

10. Thermal protection system (TPS)

11. Tracking and Data Relay System (TDRS)

B. Fill in the Blanks:

Fill in the blank with the word or words necessary to complete the statement.

1. In September 1969, the Space Task Group recommended "a _____ manned and unmanned space program."

2. The Space Shuttle system has three main elements: the _____, the _____ _____, and two _____ _____ _____.

3. The reaction control system has _____ primary and _____ secondary engines.

4. Drinkable water comes from three _____ _____ power plants.

5. The Shuttle's communication system transfers _____ _____ about its operating conditions and configurations, systems, and payloads, and _____ communications among the flight crew members and between the flight crew and ground.

6. During re-entry the thermal protection system materials protect the orbiter's outer skin from temperatures above _____ ° Fahrenheit.

7. The Shuttle's external tank has three major parts: the forward liquid-_____ tank, a non-pressurized _____, and an aft liquid-_____ tank.

8. Mission-specialist and pilot-astronaut candidates must have at least a _____ degree from an _____ institution.

9. During flight, the Shuttle commander has onboard responsibility for the
   _____, _____, mission _____, and
   _____ of flight.

10. Mission specialists do _____ _____ (space walks);
    operate the remote manipulator system, and oversee _____ and
    _____.

11. In the Mission Control Center, Houston, Texas, flight controllers watch every
    movement the crew and spacecraft make, double-check every number to be sure
    missions are proceeding as expected, and provide the expertise needed to deal
    with the _____.

C. Multiple Choice:

Circle the letter that correctly answers the question or completes the statement.

1. The Space Shuttle's mission is to transport its _____ into low-
   Earth orbit _____ to _____ kilometers above Earth.

   a. parts, 100, 200

   b. payload, 200, 400

   c. experiments, 400, 600

   d. orbiter, 1000, 2000

2. Which of the following is (are) features of the Shuttle?

   a. Up to eight crewmembers (ten in an emergency)

   b. Basic mission length is seven days

   c. Acceleration loading during launch and landing is never greater than three
      g's

   d. All of the above

3. The orbiter's three Space Shuttle Main Engines (SSMEs) are reusable, high-
   performance rocket engines that use liquid _____ to produce
   variable_____.

   a. propellant, thrust

   b. hydrazine, acceleration

   c. oxygen, velocity

   d. hydrogen, pressure

4. Which is <u>not</u> a use for the Shuttle's orbital maneuvering system?

    a. Attitude control

    b. Insert it into its orbit

    c. Orbital transfer

    d. De-orbit

5. The Environmental Control and Life Support System holds the cabin pressure close to Earth's _____-_____ with an average mixture of _____% nitrogen and _____% oxygen.

    a. mountain-level, 20, 80

    b. orbital-level, 50, 50

    c. sea-level, 80, 20

    d. Houston-level, 60, 40

6. Which of the following is (are) part of the orbiter's electrical power subsystem?

    a. Power reactant storage and distribution

    b. Secondary batteries

    c. Solar cell arrays

    d. Power conditioning and distribution

7. The two _____-_____ _____ carry the entire weight of the external tank and orbiter.

    a. light-weight tanks

    b. solid-rocket boosters

    c. anti-ballistic missiles

    d. none of the above

8. The mid-deck of the orbiter has equipment for each crew member to stow, prepare, and eat food in two categories: _____ or _____.

    a. menu, pantry

    b. dry, vacuum

    c. packaged, powdered

    d. fresh, frozen

9. The sleeping arrangements can consist of a mix of _____
   _____ and sleep restraints or rigid sleep stations.

   a. Velcro straps

   b. cockpit seats

   c. water beds

   d. sleeping bags

10. In the single system trainers, Shuttle astronauts train to operate each system,
    to _____ malfunctions, and _____ problems.

    a. correct, solve

    b. create, introduce

    c. recognize, correct

    d. supervise, avoid

11. Because the orbiter approaches landings at such a steep angle and high speed, the
    Shuttle Training Aircraft approaches with its engines in reverse _____
    and main landing gear _____.

    a. control, retracted

    b. thrust, down

    c. tracking, available

    d. direction, extended

D. Matching:

Match the item in Column A with its description in Column B. You may use an item from Column B only once, but you won't use all of them.

Column A

1.   Enterprise (OV 101) ____

2.   Endeavour ____

3.   Shuttle's payload capacity ____

4.   OMS engines' propellants ____

5.   Storage temperature of liquid hydrogen ____

6.   Intertank ____

7.   Astronaut candidates ____

8.   Motion-base flight deck ____

Column B

a.   4.6 meters by 18 meters and carries 29,000 kilograms

b.   Train in land and sea survival

c.   Minus 420° Fahrenheit

d.   Monomethyl hydrazine and nitrogen tetroxide

e.   Replacement Shuttle for Challenger

f.   Allows ground workers access as part of ground servicing

g.   Control center with 15-20 consoles

h.   Underwater training equipment

i.   Never designed to fly in space

j.   Rotates 90° to simulate liftoff and ascent

E. True/False:

Place a **T** in the blank if the statement is true, and an **F** in the blank if it is false.

_____ 1. In its return to Earth, the orbiter cannot maneuver across range.

_____ 2. The orbiter can fly in the atmosphere and land like a glider, but because it has no engines for atmospheric flight, the pilot gets only one chance to land.

_____ 3. The Tracking and Data Relay System at geostationary altitude maintains nearly continual contact with the orbiter.

_____ 4. The external tank attaches to the orbiter at five main attachment points and three secondary points.

_____ 5. The solid rocket boosters, drogue chutes, and main parachutes are retrieved by the recovery crew.

_____ 6. During a mission with one shift, all crew members sleep in shifts, so someone is always awake.

_____ 7. Astronaut candidates have few duties until assigned to a Shuttle mission.

_____ 8. The Neutral Buoyancy Laboratory simulates the weightless condition the spacecraft and crew experience during space flight.

F. Short Answers (Things to Think About):

Write a short answer to each question.

1. What are the three main parts of the Space Shuttle system?

2. Describe the purpose of the Shuttle's External Tank (ET).

3. What type of rocket is used to lift the Shuttle off the pad and power it the first two minutes of flight?

4. What type of propellant do the SSMEs use?

5. Describe the types of training that astronauts must go through.

G. List or Describe

1. Describe what you think are the most remarkable aspects of the Space Shuttle. How will it lead us into future, more routine space operations?

Chapter 15 Manned Space Explorations

Section 15.4. Case Study: Space Stations

(Homework Problems: A1-A3, B3-B6, C7-C10)

A. Define, Describe, or Identify (Vocabulary):

1. Apollo-Soyuz linkup

2. International Space Station (ISS)

3. Mir

4. Salyut 1

5. Skylab

6. Spacelab

B. Fill in the Blanks:

Fill in the blank with the word or words necessary to complete the statement.

1. In the early 1970s, NASA wanted to start understanding the _____ of lengthy space flights.

2. Skylab astronauts had triangular cleats on their shoes that fit into the mesh and _____ them to the _____.

3. The most important experiments on Skylab focused on finding how well people could _____ and _____ in space.

4. When proposed in 1964, Almaz was the first military _____ _____ in the Soviet space program.

5. _____ cosmonaut crews relieved the boredom when they arrived at the Salyut space stations in the Soyuz capsules.

6. The Shuttle-Mir Program improved our knowledge in _____, international space _____, and scientific _____.

7. For the International Space Station (ISS), Japan is building a _____ and _____ _____ vehicles.

8. The assembly in orbit of the International Space Station involves more _____ _____ than ever before and a new generation of space _____.

9. The Shuttle's Canadian-built mechanical arm has a new _____ _____ _____ that will help the operator see around corners.

10. One of the unique flight-controller positions in the ISS Mission Control Center is _____, which makes sure power is available to payloads and core systems.

C. Multiple Choice:

Circle the letter that correctly answers the question or completes the statement.

1. Space scientists wrote about the advantages of having a large space station in low-Earth orbit. Which of the following was a purpose they pointed out?

    a. Orbiting observatory and laboratory

    b. Control center for space operations

    c. Way station for trips to the Moon and planets

    d. All of the above

2. Showering on Skylab was a complicated event, because all the water needed to be _____ so it wouldn't float around the cabin.

    a. pure

    b. cold

    c. contained

    d. absorbed

3. When Skylab deployed on orbit, a part of a (an) _____
    _____ had torn loose, exposing the workshop to the Sun's rays.

    a. meteoroid shield

    b. telescope mount

    c. airlock door

    d. workshop panel

4. Skylab experiments included observing _____ to find out whether
    certain special products, such as _____ for electronic equipment
    could be produced more efficiently in the vacuum of space than on Earth.

    a. planets, valves

    b. stars, components

    c. Earth, crystals

    d. satellites, batteries

5. _____ _____ finally lowered Skylab's orbit so
    much that in 1979 it began to disintegrate at an altitude of 60 miles above sea
    level.

    a. Atmospheric drag

    b. Solar radiation

    c. Unexpected thrust

    d. Earth's bulge

6. The Apollo-Soyuz linkup was a historic event because it was the first
    _____ space operation.

    a. peaceful

    b. international

    c. docking

    d. human

7. Which of the following is <u>not</u> a country participating in the International Space
    Station?

    a. Canada

    b. Brazil

    c. Japan

    d. Argentina

8. Dealing with the real-time challenges experienced during Shuttle-Mir missions has resulted in new _____ and _____ between the U.S. and Russian space programs.

   a. cooperation, trust

   b. experiments, research

   c. growth, goodwill

   d. connection, travel

9. When completed, the International Space Station will be more than _____ times as large as Russia's Mir space station.

   a. two

   b. three

   c. four

   d. ten

10. Which of the following ISS systems is the U.S. developing?

   a. Thermal control

   b. Life support

   c. Guidance

   d. All of the above

D. Matching:

Match the item in Column A with its description in Column B. You may use an item from Column B only once, but you won't use all of them.

Column A	*Column B*
1. Skylab ____	a. Hosted cosmonauts from seven nations
2. Skylab mission durations ____	b. Recreation module
3. Soyuz 19 and Apollo 18 ____	c. Means "lightning" in Russian
4. Salyut 6 ____	d. First two modules on the ISS
5. Mir ____	e. Arm attachment for detailed maintenance tasks
6. Unity and Zarya ____	f. 28, 60, and 84 days
7. Canadian hand ____	g. Same volume as a three-bedroom house
	h. Apollo-Soyuz linkup capsules
	i. Means "peace" in Russian

E. True/False:

Place a **T** in the blank if the statement is true, and an **F** in the blank if it is false.

_____ 1. The U.S. built the Skylab cluster of modules from equipment left over from Shuttle flights.

_____ 2. To help the astronauts with orientation, engineers arranged the workshop with a feeling of "up" and "down.

_____ 3. The Apollo-Soyuz linkup was a high profile public relations exercise designed to better the relations between the two countries.

_____ 4. The Salyut 7 space station hosted the first female space traveler since 1963.

_____ 5. The Space Shuttle is the only launch vehicle capable of carrying crews to the ISS.

_____ 6. Canada, Japan, and the European Space Agency have plans to build manipulator arms for the ISS.

_____ 7. The Centrifuge Accommodation Module will simulate gravity on the ISS to compare experimental results with free-fall results.

F. Short Answers (Things to Think About):

Write a short answer to each question.

1. What was America's first space station and what were some of its early problems?

2. What was the purpose of the Apollo-Soyuz Test program?

3. Discuss some of the historical "firsts" set by early Soviet space stations.

4. What was Spacelab and which countries sponsored it?

5. What countries are involved in the International Space Station (ISS)?

6. Describe some of the research that will occur on ISS.

7. Describe one possible new location for future space stations.

G. List or Describe:

1. Has humankind received enough value from previous and current space stations to finish the ISS and plan the next generation station?